Fireworks

Witches, Spiders and Cowboys

ANTHOLOGY

Gill & Macmillan
Hume Avenue
Park West
Dublin 12
www.gillmacmillan.ie

ISBN: 9780717153183
©John Hartnett, Eithne Kennedy, Patricia O'Doherty, Eileen Phelan 2012

Design: Aisli Madden / Outburst Design
Cover Illustration: Aisli Madden
Inside Illustrations: Brian Fitzgerald, MSM Studios, Úna Woods, ODI Illustrators
Printed by Edelvives, Spain

First Published March 2012

Dear Reader,

Welcome to *Witches, Spiders and Cowboys*. This anthology is filled with a wide range of interesting fiction, poetry and non-fiction pieces. We hope you have as much fun reading this selection, as we had in putting it together.

The fiction includes extracts from lots of different kinds of stories: funny ones, sad ones, fantasies, mysteries, as well as picture books and classics. We hope that if you really like an author or a story you will go on to read the entire novel and find other titles in that genre or by the same author.

Within the non-fiction, there is a variety of pieces, from information to interviews to puzzles. You can read about topics that link up with some of the fiction themes. For example, after *The Diary of a Killer Cat*, you can find out all about Big cats. Then there are pieces relating to the kinds of reading you may have to do in order to locate information or to complete a task e.g. how to read a poster or a puzzle. These pieces have lots of photographs, tables, maps and headings to help you learn about the topic.

As well as introducing you to a range of genres, this book is designed to help you boost your reading skills and develop the strategies that good readers use. There are 'before reading', 'during reading' and 'after reading' questions or prompts to help you along the way. Let's take a look at some of these special features.

Before reading:

Think of this as a warm-up activity for reading. It is about getting your mind ready to read the text. We may ask you to make predictions about what you imagine the text will be about by checking the title, examining the artwork or photographs, scanning and reading headings, or considering what you already know about the topic or the author's style of writing.

> 1. Look at the title and the illustrations. What do you think will happen in this story?
> 2. Have you read any books by Anne Fine? Talk about it.
>
> ### The Diary of a Killer Cat

During reading:

Notice the little stars on the page. These are a signal to you to check out the prompt or question in the coloured box at the end of the page before you read on. It is also a signal to slow down your reading and to ponder this important element of the story. We might ask you to notice how the author creates a mood or how a character is feeling or why they reacted to a particular event in the story.

> And maybe the stains won't come out, ever. ☆
> So *hang* me.
>
> What kind of cat is Tuffy? Why do you think this?
>
> Why was there such a fuss?

After reading (fiction):

Notice the icons on the left-hand side. They are a signal to you that you have to think differently in order to answer the question.

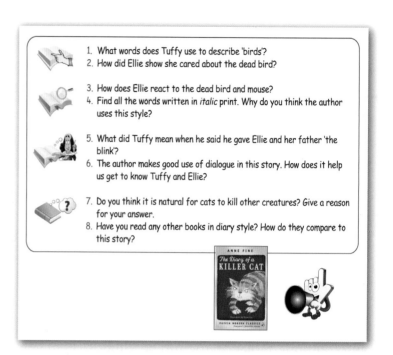

1. What words does Tuffy use to describe 'birds'?
2. How did Ellie show she cared about the dead bird?

3. How does Ellie react to the dead bird and mouse?
4. Find all the words written in *italic* print. Why do you think the author uses this style?

5. What did Tuffy mean when he said he gave Ellie and her father 'the blink'?
6. The author makes good use of dialogue in this story. How does it help us get to know Tuffy and Ellie?

7. Do you think it is natural for cats to kill other creatures? Give a reason for your answer.
8. Have you read any other books in diary style? How do they compare to this story?

 These questions ask you to recall details from the story. There is only one right answer and you can find it in one particular spot in the story.

 These questions also ask you to recall some details from the story. The answer is in the text but you will have to find it in different parts of the story and put it all together to respond correctly. This section may also draw attention to particular words or phrases in the story.

 These questions ask you to read between the lines. This means the question cannot be answered directly from the text and there is no one right answer. These questions are great 'conversation starters'. You may also find your answer or opinion differs to that of your classmates. You will need to back up your answer with evidence from the text, so you may have to re-read parts of the story and think deeply about these questions.

 These questions also relate to the story but go beyond it. The answer is not in the text. In fact, you could answer the question without having read the text. They are 'real world' questions that may ask you to think about the theme of the story or a particular topic or issue. These too are great 'conversation starters'.

At the end of each extract, we have (where possible) included the cover of the book it was taken from and earmarked if an audio recording of this extract is available on our website: www.fireworksenglish.ie

So happy reading, thinking and debating... go have some fun; lose yourself in a story, a poem or discover something new in an information piece.

Contents

The Diary of a Killer Cat

Anne Fine

Monday

Okay, okay. So hang me. I killed the bird. For pity's sake, I'm a *cat*. It's practically my *job* to go creeping round the garden after sweet little eensyweensy birdy-pies that can hardly fly from one hedge to another. So what am I supposed to do when one of the poor feathery little flutterballs just about throws itself into my mouth? I mean, it practically landed on my paws. It could have *hurt* me.

Okay, *okay*. So I biffed it. Is that any reason for Ellie to cry in my fur so hard I almost *drown*, and squeeze me so hard I almost *choke*?

'Oh, Tuffy!' she says, all sniffles and red eyes and piles of wet tissues. 'Oh, Tuffy. How could you *do* that?'

How could I *do* that? I'm a *cat*. How did I know there was going to be such a giant great fuss, with Ellie's mother rushing off to fetch sheets of old newspaper, and Ellie's father filling a bucket with soapy water?

Okay, *okay*. So maybe I shouldn't have dragged it in and left it on the carpet. And maybe the stains won't come out, ever.

So *hang* me.

What kind of cat is Tuffy? Why do you think this?

Why was there such a fuss?

Tuesday

I quite enjoyed the little funeral. I don't think they really wanted me to come, but, after all, it's just as much my garden as theirs. In fact, I spend a whole lot more time in it than they do. I'm the only one in the family who uses it properly. Not that they're grateful. You ought to hear them.

'That cat is *ruining* my flower beds. There are hardly any of the petunias left.'

'I'd barely *planted* the lobelias before it was lying on top of them, squashing them flat.'

'I *do* wish it wouldn't dig holes in the anemones.' ⭐

Moan, moan, moan, moan. I don't know why they bother to keep a cat, since all they ever seem to do is complain.

All except Ellie. She was too busy being soppy about the bird. She put it in a ⭐ box, and packed it round with cotton wool, and dug a little hole, and then we all stood round it while she said a few words, wishing the bird luck in heaven.

> ⭐ Who do you think complains about the cat?

> ⭐ Do you agree with Tuffy that Ellie was being soppy?

'Go away,' Ellie's father hissed at me. (I find that man quite rude.) But I just flicked my tail at him. Gave him the blink. Who does he think he is? If I want to watch a little birdy's funeral, I'll watch it. After all, I've known the bird longer than any of them have. I knew it when it was alive.

Wednesday

So spank me! I brought a dead mouse into their precious house. I didn't even kill it. When I came across it, it was already a goner. Nobody's safe around here. ✦ This avenue is ankle-deep in rat poison, fast cars charge up and down at all hours, and I'm not the only cat around here. I don't even know what happened to the thing. All I know is, I found it. It was already dead. (Fresh dead, but dead.) And at the time I thought it was a good idea to bring it home. Don't ask me why. I must have been crazy. How did I know that Ellie was going to grab me and give me one of her little talks?

'Oh, Tuffy! That's the second time this week. I can't bear it. I know you're a cat, and it's natural and everything. But please, for my sake, stop.'

She gazed into my eyes.

'Will you stop? Please?'

I gave her the blink. (Well, I tried. But she wasn't having any.)

'I *mean* it, Tuffy,' she told me. 'I love you, and I understand how you feel. But you've got to stop doing this, okay?'

She had me by the paws. What could I say? So I tried to look all sorry. And then she burst into tears all over again, and we had another funeral.

This place is turning into Fun City. It really is.

✦ Do you believe Tuffy? Why?

3

1. What words does Tuffy use to describe birds?
2. How did Ellie show she cared about the dead bird?
3. What flowers were planted in the garden?

4. How does Ellie react to the dead bird and mouse?
5. Find all the words written in *italic* print. Why do you think the author uses this style?

6. What did Tuffy mean when he said he gave Ellie and her father 'the blink'?
7. The author makes good use of dialogue in this story. How does it help us get to know Tuffy and Ellie?
8. Is Tuffy's version of events believable? Give a reason for your answer.
9. If Ellie kept a diary how would her entry for Wednesday have been different from Tuffy's?
10. What do you think Tuffy might have written about on Thursday?

11. Do you think it is natural for cats to kill other creatures? Give a reason for your answer.
12. Have you read any other books in diary style? How do they compare to this story?

ANNE FINE

The Diary of a
KILLER CAT

PUFFIN MODERN CLASSICS
Everyone's favourite stories

Big cats

1. How many kinds of big cat can you name?
2. Look at the pictures and discuss what you know about each big cat.

There are 37 kinds of cat in the world but only seven are classified as big cats. These are the lion, tiger, cheetah, puma, jaguar, leopard and snow leopard. They are found in Africa, Asia and North and South America. Many of these animals are under threat today.

Leopards

The leopard's spotted coat is a perfect camouflage in the forests and grasslands. This allows it to steal up close enough to pounce on its prey of antelope, deer or wild pig. The leopard is a strong climber and often drags its dead prey high up into the branches of a tree to dine in peace. It is one of the few cats that likes water. Females usually give birth to two cubs. Cubs are born with their eyes closed. They are grey in colour with their body markings not yet clearly visible. The mother protects her cubs, often moving them from one hiding place to the next until they are old enough to learn how to fend for themselves. They live with their mother for up to two years.

Snow leopards

A snow leopard's hairy coat is paler in colour than a leopard's and is dotted with dark spots and streaks. This helps it to blend in with the snow and rocks in the snowy Asian mountains. It is well adapted to its harsh environment. Its thick coat protects it against the cold and its wide feet are like snowshoes, helping

it to pad along in the snow. Its tail is longer than a leopard's, which makes it easier to balance in its rocky habitat. It feeds mainly on sheep in the Himalayan mountains but can kill prey up to three times its size.

Jaguars

The jaguar looks like a leopard but it is larger. Its coat is light tan or orange in colour. Its markings are black rosettes with black spots in the middle. Its name comes from a Native American word 'yaguar', meaning, 'he who kills with one leap'. Its chunky sturdy limbs make it a skilful climber and swimmer. On land it stalks deer and tapirs. A tapir is an animal like a wild pig. In water it feeds on fish, turtles, or caimans. A caiman is a small animal like an alligator. The jaguar is a solitary animal and marks its territory with urine and by clawing trees. Females give birth to between one and four cubs at a time. They remain with their mother for up two years.

Cheetahs

The cheetah also looks like a leopard. It is the world's fastest land mammal. It can run at speeds of up to 100 kilometers per hour (kph) and can increase speed from 0 to 96 kph in just three seconds. That is faster than many cars. Unlike most other big cats, it hunts during the day. Its body markings, remarkable eyesight and speed all help to make the cheetah an excellent hunter. It hides itself in the long grass of the African plains and scans the territory for movement. After it selects its prey, it launches its agile body twisting and turning easily, as it chases a gazelle, wildebeest or zebra. It often hauls its prey to a cool sheltered location. It only needs to drink every three to four days, another advantage in a tough hot habitat. Female cheetahs usually give birth to three cubs at a time. They remain with their mother for up to two years.

Spot the difference!

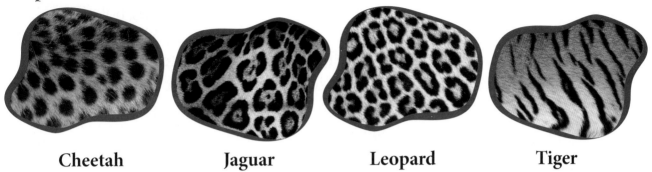

Cheetah   **Jaguar**   **Leopard**   **Tiger**

Pumas

Pumas are also known as mountain lions and cougars. They are mostly a light tan in colour. They live in different habitats ranging from the swamps in Florida to the mountains and forest of North and South America. Pumas hunt at dawn, dusk and through the night, stalking deer, coyote, porcupine, and raccoon. They are muscular and have a powerful leap that allows them to jump on prey, which they kill with a bite to the back of the neck. They drag the kill to a safe place where they feed on it for several days. Pumas are shy creatures who live alone and hunt over a territory covering up to 78 square kilometres. Females have up to six cubs in a litter.

Lions

Most lions can be found in Africa. Their coat is usually a light yellow in colour and their tails have a tuft of hair on the end. Males have an impressive shaggy mane. Lions live in groups

called prides. A pride usually has up to three males, several lionesses and their cubs who stay with their parents for up to three years. Young females usually stay in the pride while the young males leave to form a pride of their own. Lions mark their territory with urine and by scratching the ground. Their territory can stretch up to 260 square kilometres and usually includes a watering hole. They roar to warn other lions to stay away. An adult lion's roar can be heard up to eight kilometres away. Lionesses do all of the hunting and work in teams to trap their prey, which includes wildebeest, impala, zebra, and buffalo. Adult lions feed first and cubs are last to the table. They pass the day sleeping, resting or grooming and save their energy for hunting at night.

Tigers

Tigers have very distinctive coats which are mostly orange in colour and marked with dark stripes. These patterns are like a fingerprint and help to tell one tiger from another. A century ago there were eight kinds of tiger but now only five exist. Bengal tigers are the most common and are found in  India. They hunt alone at night and blend in well with their habitat. They prowl the jungle and creep quietly up on their prey before springing upon them at close range. They feed mainly on buffalo, deer and wild pigs and can eat up to 27 kilogrammes of meat in one sitting. They are superb swimmers and love to bathe. Females give birth to between two and six cubs at a time. Cubs do not hunt until they are about 18 months old and usually remain with their mother for two to three years.

	Weight in kg	Location	Habitat	Life span in years
African Lion	120-191	Africa	Grassland, Desert	12-16
Tiger	109-227	Asia	Jungle, Near water	8-10
Cheetah	35-65	Africa, Asia	Desert, Grassland	10-12
Puma	53-100	North/South America	Swamp, Forest, Mountain,	8-13
Jaguar	45-113	North/South America	Jungle, Near water	12-15
Leopard	30-80	Asia, Africa	Forest, Desert, Mountain, Grassland	12-17
Snow leopard	35-55	Asia	Mountain	15-18

1. Choose any two big cats. Compare and contrast them by:
   a.) body markings
   b.) how they hunt
   c.) what they eat
   d.) habitats
   e.) their young.
2. Arrange the big cats in order of their weight starting with the lightest.
3. Which big cat usually lives the longest?
4. Why is the cheetah one of the few big cats to hunt during the day?
5. Scan the text and name all the animals mentioned in this piece. Choose one and find out more about it. The headings in question 1 will help you.
6. Find out why the big cats are under threat. Look up a website such as www.kids.nationalgeographic.com

Blake's Tyger – Revisited

Michaela Morgan

*On hearing that tigers in captivity can gradually
lose their colour, losing their camouflaging stripes
and fading gradually to white.*

Tiger! Tiger! Turning white
In a cage just twice your height
Six paces left, six paces right,
A long slow day, a longer night.

Tiger! Tiger! Dreaming still
Of the scent? The chase? The Kill?
And now? No need. No place. No scope.
No space. No point. No hope.

Tiger! Tiger! Paces. Paces.
Once he flashed through open spaces.
His world once echoed to his roars.
Now he's quiet. He stares. He snores.

An inch of sky glimpsed through the bars.
A puddle. Concrete. Smells of cars.
He sniffs the air. He slumps. He sighs.
And stares and stares through jaundiced eyes.

Dad and the Cat and the Tree

Kit Wright

This morning a cat got
Stuck in our tree.
Dad said, 'Right just
Leave it to me.'

The tree was wobbly,
The tree was tall.
Mum said, 'For goodness'
Sake don't fall!'

'Fall?' scoffed Dad,
'A climber like me?
Child's play this is!
You wait and see.'

He got out the ladder
from the garden shed.
It slipped. He landed
In the flower bed.

'Never mind,' said Dad,
Brushing the dirt
Off his hair and his face
And his trousers and shirt.

'We'll try Plan B. Stand
Out of the way!'
Mum said, 'Don't fall
Again, OK?'

11

'Fall again?' said Dad.
'Funny joke!'
Then he swung himself up
On a branch. It broke.

Dad landed, *wallop*
Back on the deck.
Mum said, 'Stop it!
You'll break your neck!'

'Rubbish!' said Dad.
'Now we try Plan C.
Easy as winking
To a climber like me!'

Then he climbed up high
On the garden wall.
Guess what?
He *didn't fall*!

He gave a great leap
and he landed flat
In the crook of the tree trunk –
Right on the cat!

The cat gave a yell
and sprang to the ground,
Pleased as punch to be
Safe and sound.

So it's smiling and smirking,
Smug as can be,
But poor old Dad's
Still

Stuck
Up
The
Tree!

Popcorn

Look at these statements and say if you think they are true or false:
a.) Popcorn is a new kind of food.
b.) A popped corn kernel can expand to 30 times its original size.
c.) Popcorn was used to tell fortunes.
d.) Corn was first grown in Russia.

Many people enjoy a tub of popcorn when they go to the cinema. We think of popcorn as a new kind of food, but did you know that popcorn has been around for thousands of years? Archaeologists think that corn was first grown in Mexico. The oldest kernels of popcorn were found in the Bat Caves in Mexico about 60 years ago. They were over 5000 years old and they were still able to pop!

How did people first learn to pop corn? Maybe someone dropped some corn kernels in the fire by accident. The heat would have turned the kernels into popcorn. Later people put kernels in a pot and placed the pot on heated sand.

In ancient times people used the kernels in many ways. They not only ate popcorn, they used it to decorate their head-dresses and as ornaments on statues of their gods. They even used popcorn to tell their fortunes by tossing corn kernels into a fire. They examined how the corn fell to make their predictions.

When Christopher Columbus arrived in the New World in 1492, he saw the Native Americans using popcorn. In his diary he wrote that they tried to sell some to his sailors.

In 1885, an American called Charles Cretors changed the popping of corn forever. He invented a corn-popping machine. His invention became very popular and soon the machines were in every cinema and corner shop popping corn on the spot!

What makes popcorn pop?

Popcorn kernels contain starch and moisture. When the kernels are heated the moisture turns into steam. The steam is trapped inside the hard shell of the kernel. The pressure grows until it bursts the shell. The steam escapes and the starchy inside pops out. A popped corn kernel can grow to as much as thirty times its original size.

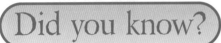

Did you know?

Plain popcorn is a healthy snack food. It contains lots of fibre and very little fat or sugar.

The world's largest popcorn ball was made in October, 2006 in the USA. It weighed more than one and a half kilogrammes and was two and a half metres wide.

In ancient times, people made popcorn soup and popcorn beer.

Today Americans eat more than half a billion kilogrammes of popcorn every year.

In 2009 archaeologists were digging up the remains of a 300-year-old theatre in Dublin. Among the things they found in the ruins were oyster shells. People visiting the Smock Alley Theatre clearly enjoyed oysters more than popcorn as a snack!

How to pop corn

You will need:

- a large, heavy-bottomed saucepan with a lid
- 1 tablespoon of vegetable oil
- 3 tablespoons of fresh popcorn

1. Put the oil in the pan and heat it over a high heat. Ask an adult to help you.
2. Swirl the oil over the base of the pan. Pour in the kernels and put the lid on.
3. Shake the saucepan often. Do not lift the lid, but let it rattle so that the steam can escape.
4. Put the popped corn into a bowl and remove any unpopped kernels.

Flavour your popcorn!

Cinnamon popcorn
Add one tablespoon of melted butter mixed with two tablespoons of sugar and half a teaspoon of cinnamon.

Cheesy popcorn
Add two tablespoons of melted butter mixed with two to three tablespoons of grated cheese.

Trickle your flavouring over the popcorn while it is still hot and stir.

1. Look back at the true/false statements on page 14. What did you learn? Can you make some true and false questions of your own?
2. Invent your own flavour for popcorn.

1. Read the introduction. Look at the pictures and read the speech bubbles. What do you think will happen in the extract?
2. Have you ever kept a diary?
3. Do you like the way this story is presented? How is it different from other stories in this book?

Diary of a Wimpy Kid:
The Last Straw

Jeff Kinney

Greg is a ten-year-old boy who lives in America. He keeps a very funny diary about his life. In this extract, he tells about the time the teacher's dictionary went missing in class.

Yesterday I actually got a 'zero' on a quiz in Geography. But, in my defence, it was really hard to study for the quiz and watch football at the same time.

To be honest with you, I don't think teachers should be making us memorize all this stuff to begin with, because in the future everyone is going to have a personal robot that tells you whatever you need to know. ☆

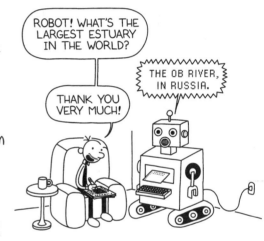

Speaking of teachers, today Mrs Craig was in a really bad mood. That's because the big dictionary that usually sits on her desk was missing.

I'm sure someone just borrowed it and forgot to put it back, but the word Mrs Craig kept using was 'stole'.

Mrs Craig said that if the dictionary wasn't returned to her desk before the end of the period she was keeping everyone inside for recess.

☆ Do you agree with Greg?

Then she told us she was going to leave the room, and that if the 'culprit' returned the dictionary to her desk there wouldn't be any consequences, and there would be no questions asked.

Mrs Craig made Patty Farrell class monitor and left the room. Patty takes her job as class monitor really seriously, and when she's in charge nobody dares to step out of line.

I was just hoping the person who took the dictionary would hurry up and come clean, because I had two cartons of chocolate milk for lunch.

But nobody did come forward. And, sure enough, Mrs Craig stuck to her promise and kept us inside for recess. Then she said she was gonna keep us inside every day until the dictionary was returned.

Friday

Mrs Craig has kept us inside for the past three days, and still no dictionary. Today Patty Farrell was sick, so Mrs Craig put Alex Aruda in charge of the room while she was gone.

Alex is a good student, but people aren't afraid of Alex the way they are of Patty Farrell. As soon as Mrs Craig left the room, it was complete pandemonium.

A couple of guys who were sick of getting stuck inside for recess every day decided to try to figure out who took Mrs Craig's dictionary.

✩ Do you believe Mrs Craig? Why?

18

The first person they interrogated was this kid named Corey Lamb. I think Corey was number one on the list of suspects because he's smart and he's always using big words.

Corey fessed up to the crime in no time flat. But it turns out he only said he did it because the pressure made him crack. ⭐

SHAKE SHAKE

SUCK SUCK

The next kid on the list was Peter Lynn, and before you knew it Peter was confessing, too.

I figured it was just a matter of time before those guys cornered ME. So I knew I had to think up something fast.

SQUEAL!

I've read enough Sherlock Sammy books to know that sometimes it takes a nerd to get you out of a pinch. And I figured if anyone could crack this case it was Alex Aruda. ⭐

So me and a couple of other guys who were worried about getting hassled went over to Alex to see if he could help us out.

We told Alex we needed him to solve the mystery of who took Mrs Craig's dictionary, but he didn't even know what we were TALKING about. I guess Alex had been so wrapped up in his book that he hadn't even noticed what had been going on around him for the past couple of days.

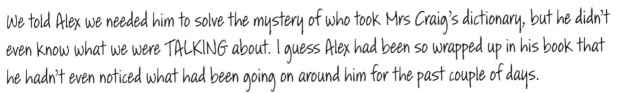

⭐ Would you have confessed if you were Corey?

⭐ What kind of books are Sherlock Sammy books, do you think?

Plus, Alex always stays inside to read during recess, so Mrs Craig's punishment hadn't had a big effect on his life.

Unfortunately, Alex has read his share of Sherlock Sammy books, too, so he said he would help us if we paid him five bucks. Well, that was totally unfair, because Sherlock Sammy only charges a nickel. But me and the other guys agreed it was worth it, and we pooled our money, then forked over the five dollars.

We laid out all the facts of the case to Alex, but we didn't know a whole lot. Then we asked Alex if he could get us pointed in the right direction.

I expected Alex to start taking notes and spout some scientific mumbo jumbo, but all he did was close the book he was reading and show the cover to us. And you're not gonna BELIEVE this, but it was Mrs Craig's dictionary.

Alex said he'd been studying the dictionary to get ready for the state spelling bee next month. Well, THAT would've been nice to know BEFORE we gave him our five bucks. Anyway, there was no time to waste complaining, because Mrs Craig was gonna be back in the room at any second. ⭐

⭐ **What do you think will happen when Mrs Craig comes back into the class?**

1. What did Mrs Craig say would happen if the dictionary was not returned before the end of the period (class)?
2. Why did Greg want the dictionary to be returned quickly?
3. Why did Alex Aruda take the dictionary?

4. Find all the words used in the text that signal this story is set in America. What words would we use in Ireland instead?
5. How did the class react differently to the two monitors? Why do you think this happened?

6. Do you think Greg works hard in class? Why do you think this?
7. What do you think Greg would have done if the two boys had 'cornered' him?
8. Would you like to have a teacher like Mrs Craig? Why?
9. Do you think Mrs Craig was aware of what was going on while she was out of the room? Give a reason for your answer.
10. Would you like to be in Greg's class? Why?

11. Have you ever confessed to something you didn't do? Talk about it.
12. Would you like to be left in charge of your class? Why?

Using a dictionary

A dictionary contains lists of words and their meanings, in alphabetical order. You can use a dictionary to find out what a word means, but there are other things you can use it for. For example, you can use a dictionary to check that you have spelt a word correctly or used a word in the right way.

Imagine you want to look up the word dinghy for example. You know it means 'a small boat' but you're not sure of the spelling.

> The blue words at the top of the page are called 'guide words.' They help to narrow down your search. Every word on a page is arranged alphabetically between the two guide words. The word 'dinghy' for example comes between these two words in alphabetical order so you know to look for it on this page
>
> diminish   dirty

> The next word after each dictionary entry tells you which part of speech it is, for example, noun, adjective, verb...

> Not all dictionaries have exactly the same detail or format. Some may have illustrations. This dictionary uses a blue box to highlight different details, for example, to tell you where a word comes from, or to highlight a word that has a similar spelling or sound.

diminish

diminish VERB **diminishes, diminishing, diminished** to get or make less or smaller

dimple NOUN **dimples** a small hollow like dent in the skin of your chin or cheek: He has dimples when he smiles.

din NOUN a very loud noise

dine VERB **dines, dining, dined** to have dinner

diner NOUN **diners 1** someone who is eating dinner, especially in a restaurant **2** in the US, a restaurant like a motorway service station

dinghy NOUN **dinghies** a small boat for rowing or sailing

dinner NOUN **dinners** a main meal in the evening or in the middle of the day

dinosaur NOUN **dinosaurs** an extinct prehistoric giant reptile

- **dinosaur** comes from the Greek for 'terrible lizard'.

dip VERB **dips, dipping, dipped 1** to put something in and out of a liquid quickly: *Dip the clothes in the dye.* **2** to slope downwards: *The field dips down towards the bottom of the valley.* **3** to dip a vehicle's headlights is to lower them so that they are not dazzling to other drivers
NOUN **dips**
1 a liquid that something can be put into for a short time
2 a slope downwards in the land
3 a quick swim
4 a soft food that you eat by dipping things in it

diploma NOUN **diplomas** a qualification that someone can study for in a particular subject

diplomacy NOUN **1** communication between countries **2** managing to deal with people without offending them

- **diplomat** NOUN **diplomats** a person whose job is to keep good relationships and communications between countries

- **diplomatic** ADJECTIVE **1** to do with the relationships between countries: *the diplomatic service* **2** If you are diplomatic, you are careful not to say things which will offend or upset someone

dire ADJECTIVE **dreadful**: *in dire need*

direct ADJECTIVE **1** straight, or as straight as possible: *a direct route to the airport* **2** frank and honest
VERB **directs, directing, directed 1** to aim or make something go a particular way: *Their weapons were directed at us.* **2** to tell someone how to get somewhere: *Could you please direct me to the post office?* **3** to control or guide something: *The police direct the traffic when it's busy.*

directly ADVERB **1** straight away: *The manager will see you directly.* **2** straight: *looking directly at me*

directness NOUN being frank and honest with people: *Geraldine's directness sometimes seems like rudeness.*

direction NOUN **directions**
1 direction is controlling or organizing
2 a direction is the place or point a thing or person goes towards or faces: *Which direction is the library?*
3 a direction is an order or instruction: *a list of directions on the side of the packet*
4 directions are instructions for getting somewhere: *Try to follow my directions to the hidden treasure.*

director NOUN **directors 1** the manager of a business **2** a person who makes a film or organizes a stage show

directory NOUN **directories 1** a book that tells you people's names, addresses and telephone numbers **2** (ICT) a group of computer files with a particular name: *Put this file in the letters directory.*

direct speech NOUN (*grammar*) in a story or report, direct speech tells you the actual words that a person said. Look up and compare **indirect speech**

dirt NOUN any substance that is not clean or makes something unclean, such as mud or dust

dirty ADJECTIVE **dirtier, dirtiest 1** not clean: *dirty floors* **2** not polite: *dirty*

Aa
Bb
Cc
Dd
Ee
Ff
Gg
Hh
Ii
Jj
Kk
Ll
Mm
Nn
Oo
Pp
Qq
Rr
Ss
Tt
Uu
Vv
Ww
Xx
Yy
Zz

A word in **black** after NOUN is the plural of the noun. This is the word you use when you are talking about more than one of something.
dinghy NOUN **dinghies**
direction NOUN **directions**.

Words in **black** after VERB show you how to spell the different forms of the verb. The one you use depends on who did the action or when it happened.
direct VERB **directs**, **directing**, **directed**

Words in **black** after ADJECTIVE are the ones you use when you are making a comparison and you want to say something is *more* or *the most*.
dirty ADJECTIVE **dirtier**, **dirtiest**

Numbers show you that there are different meanings of the word. Each meaning has a different number. After each number the meaning of each word is explained. This is called the *definition* of the word.

The words in *italics* show you how you might use the main word. The examples can help to make the meaning clearer.

The alphabet down the side of the page will help you locate words beginning with the letter you are looking for. For example on this page the letter D is highlighted because the word we are looking for is 'dinghy': Aa Bb Cc Dd Ee

Picking Teams

Allan Ahlberg

When we pick teams in the playground,
Whatever the game might be,
There's always somebody left till last
And usually it's me.
I stand there looking hopeful
And tapping myself on the chest,
But the captains pick the others first,
Starting, of course, with the best.
Maybe if teams were sometimes picked
Starting with the worst,
Once in his life a boy like me
Could end up being first!

Girl in Goal

Rob Childs

1

'Can I play?'
The boys looked round in surprise. They were about to pick sides for their lunchtime kickabout.
'Go on, let me play in goal.'
'You must be joking,' said Ben, captain of Gateway Juniors soccer team.
'Girls are no good at football. Clear off, Samantha.'
She stayed where she was.
'They called me Sam at my old school.'
The footballers grinned at each other and waited to see what Ben would do. He didn't want to be shown up by this new girl in front of all his mates. She was bigger than him and he didn't fancy the idea of trying to get rid of her by force.
He decided to give way – just a little.
'OK, then ... I'll call you Sam,' he sighed, 'but you still can't play in our game.'
The boys all laughed and Sam went off to sulk against the nearby wall. But she was not the kind of girl to give up that easily. As soon as the game started, she wandered back to stand behind one of the goals.
Sam loved goalkeeping. Ever since she could remember, Dad had played football with her in the garden, taking shots at her in their home-made goal. Now she could catch a ball better than him!

25

Sam watched as different boys took their turn as goalie between the piles of coats. None of them, it seemed to her, really wanted to play in goal. Two even let in shots on purpose so they could go back out on the field.

Suddenly, Ben lashed in a beauty. It was struck with such power that the ball flew past the goalkeeper before he made a move.

But not past Sam! Out of habit, she leapt up and snatched the ball cleanly out of the air. Her spectacular catch did not go unnoticed, although Ben was already well into his goal celebrations. He danced away, punching the air, and then posed for the television cameras as if he'd just scored the winner at Wembley.

Gareth, the school team's centre-back, had seen Ben's antics before. He was staring in amazement towards Sam instead.

'Hey, maybe she's not too bad after all,' he thought, then checked himself. 'Well, for a girl, that is!' ✮

2

When the bell went, the footballers trailed in for afternoon school and Sam plucked up the courage to confront Ben.

'What have you got against girls playing football?'

'Cos it's a man's game. It ain't meant for girls,' he snarled, brushing past her. 'Anyway, it's my ball. I can decide who I want to play with it.'

Sam realised that one of the boys was hanging back.

'Old Nozza runs the school footy team,' he said to her. 'You'll have to try and show him what you can do.'

'Nozza? Who's that?' she asked.

'His real name is Mr Norris. He used to teach here but now he's retired. He's dead keen on football so he still comes in to coach the team.'

'What's your name?' asked Sam.

'Gareth, but just call me Gaz. All my mates do.'

'Thanks, Gaz. What's the team like this season?'

Gareth chuckled. 'Gateway are the strongest team in the league. We're bottom, holding everybody else up!'

✮ At the end of each section pause and answer these questions:
1. What is the main thing that happened in this section?
2. What do you learn about the characters in the section?
3. What do you think will happen next?

It was an old joke, but Sam still laughed.

'Sounds like you need some girls in it,' she grinned.

'Don't reckon old Nozza would approve,' he said, shaking his head. 'He's like Ben. They both think girls and football don't mix.'

'That's stupid. Loads of girls play for their schools at soccer nowadays.'

'The reason we're bottom of the league is 'cos we've been letting too many goals in. What the team really needs is a decent keeper ...'

'Maybe there's hope for me,' said Sam, as they went into the classroom.

When Gareth sat down, Ben sneered at him. 'I saw you, talking to that girl. What have you been saying to her?'

'Nothing. Just telling her to bring her kit for PE tomorrow, that's all.'

'Netball kit, I hope.'

Much to Sam's disgust, she did have to play netball. She'd changed into her bright yellow goalie top, with matching cap and gloves, but her teacher insisted that she practised with the rest of the girls.

Sam watched with envy as Mr Norris led the boys over to the playing field. Ben pointed towards her and laughed.

She sighed and grabbed the red GK bib before anyone else could claim it. She was still determined to play as goalkeeper, even in netball.

Sam used her extra height to good advantage in the goal circle. Nobody could outjump her and her catching was excellent. The shooter hardly had a touch of the ball.

The teacher was very impressed. 'To think you wanted to go off and play with the boys,' she laughed. 'What a waste! You're the best goalkeeper of your age I've ever seen.'

It was a nice compliment, but Sam wished that Mr Norris had said it to her instead. ⭐

3

Ben was away the next day and Gareth invited Sam to play at lunchtime. The other boys didn't object. She was the only one who had brought a football to school.

Gareth picked Sam for his team immediately, causing an outbreak of giggles and jokes among his mates.

'She your girlfriend or something, Gaz?' smirked Jack, Gateway's leading scorer

and rival team captain for the day.

'She's my goalkeeper,' he replied. 'Bet you don't score past her.'

'Easy. What d'yer want to bet?'

Gareth thought quickly. 'If you manage to score, you can have my new computer game for a week. And if you don't I can have one of yours.'

Jack grinned. 'OK, you're on. I'll come round to your place and collect it after school.'

'Right, Sam, you know what's at stake,' Gareth said.

'What, your game?'

'No, I don't care about that. This is your big chance to prove to this lot how good you are in goal.'

Jack tested her out straight away. His low shot bounced awkwardly in front of her, but Sam made sure her body was well behind the ball. It bobbled up, struck her on the shoulder and rolled wide of the coats.

'Good stop!' cried Gareth.

'Lucky, you mean,' snorted Jack. 'Next time, you wait.'

He soon found out that Sam's goalkeeping didn't rely on luck. She'd only been beaten once and Jack wasn't the scorer. Sam had pulled off several saves at his expense and her side were winning 4–1.

The longer the game went on, the redder Jack's face became with frustration and embarrassment. Finally, his blushes were saved by the bell. Distracted for a moment by its loud rings, Sam let Jack's last desperate shot skid under her dive.

'Time was up. Doesn't count,' she yelled crossly.

'Rubbish!' Jack retorted. 'Game's not over till we pack up. That was a goal.'

'Doesn't matter, Sam, forget it,' Gareth told her. 'You've shown them what you can do, that's the main thing.'

'Yeah, but Nozza doesn't know yet,' she said.

Gareth grinned. 'Looks like we'll have to make sure he finds out. We've got a soccer practice tomorrow after school, so come prepared – and bring your cap.'

'My goalie cap? I don't see...'

'Nor will old Nozza,' Gareth laughed. 'I've just come up with a brilliant plan. Listen...'

4

'You say this newcomer is a useful goalkeeper,' said Mr Norris before the practice began.

'Yes,' said Gareth. 'Sam's the name. Played in goal at a previous school.'

Mr Norris gazed across to where Jack was taking shots at the tall figure in the yellow outfit. 'Hmm, seems to know how to handle a ball,' he murmured. 'Right, let's see what this er... Sam can do, shall we?'

Gareth breathed a sigh of relief and went to break the good news to her. 'OK so far. He doesn't suspect anything – yet. Just keep that cap pulled down real tight so old Nozza doesn't get a proper look at you.'

Jack laughed. 'Good job Ben's still away. We could never have tried to pull a stunt like this with him around.'

Mr Norris stood on the touchline to watch the practice match. Every so often, he'd blow his whistle to halt play and bellow at somebody for making a mistake.

Praise was rare, but he actually clapped when Sam dived full-length to tip a rising shot over the crossbar. The boys could hardly believe it.

'He must like you,' chuckled Gareth.

'He won't when he finds out who Sam really is,' Jack cut in. 'He'll be dead mad, being made to look a fool.'

Sam had no chance to worry about that. She was kept much too busy, producing a number of fine saves. By the end of the session, her kit and face were smothered in mud.

'Not a pretty sight!' joked Gareth, just managing to dodge Sam's playful swipe in time.

Only once had her cap come off. It happened during a goalmouth scramble with Mr Norris standing nearby, but he had not seemed to notice anything strange.

'Home time, gather round,' he called out and the players trotted up to him, dying to hear what he was going to say about Sam. The trick seemed to have worked a treat.

'Er ... have you picked the team for the next game yet, sir?' asked Gareth.

'You mean, will our new star goalie be playing?' said Mr Norris. Then he smiled and leant over to lift Sam's cap gently off her head.

'Of course. I've already heard all about Samantha's talents in netball. No reason why she can't play for Gateway in both sports, is there?'

Mr Norris strode off, whistling to himself, leaving a group of stunned footballers gaping at each other.

'It's us who've been made fools of,' laughed Gareth. 'Old Nozza must have known what we were up to all along.' ⭐

1. Why would Ben not let Sam play football with them?
2. According to Gaz, why was the school football team bottom of the league?
3. What bet did Gaz make with Jack?

4. What sentences tell you that Ben was the leader of the group?
5. Skim the text to find evidence that Sam is a good goalie.

6. Do you think Nozza knew who Sam was right from the start? Which sentence hints at this?
7. Authors often have contrasting characters in a story. How are Ben and Gaza different?
8. Are Ben and Sam similar in any way?
9. Can you think of a reason why Ben might not have been happy to have a girl as goalkeeper?
10. Do any of the characters change in any way during the story? If so, how are they different and what changes them?

11. Have you ever changed your opinion about something? Talk about it.

All about soccer

1. What do you know about soccer?
2. Do you have a player/club/country that you support?

Soccer has been played in different forms since ancient times. About 2000 years ago, the people of Ancient Greece played it using a ball stuffed with animal hair! The Inuit or Eskimos used to play it on ice using balls stuffed with grass, caribou hair or moss. They called it *aqsaqtuk*.

A game like soccer was played long ago in China. The first game was said to have been played to celebrate the Emperor's birthday. A ball made of horsehair was used. According to legend, the winning team was rewarded with a magnificent feast. The losing team had their heads cut off! Soccer as we know it today came into being about 150 years ago. Today, it is the most watched and played sport in the world with a following of almost three billion people.

FIFA World Cup trophy

Soccer timeline

1866 Length of the game is fixed at 90 minutes

1872 Corner kick is introduced

1874 Shin guards are used for the first time

1875 Teams change ends at half-time instead of after every goal

1878 Referee's whistle is introduced

1890 Goal nets are used for the first time

1891 Penalty kick is introduced

1930 The first World Cup is held in Uruguay

1965 Substitutes are used for the first time in league matches

1970 The first red and yellow cards are used in World Cup games

1996 The first Women's Olympic soccer final takes place

2002 The World Cup is held in an African country for the first time (South Africa)

In 1997, Iran beat The Maldives 17-0. This is the highest score ever in a World Cup qualifying match.

In 1998, Kenyan soccer coach, Allan Abuto Nyajong, kept a football in the air for 16 hours and 27 minutes!

In 1960, a referee in Denmark was just about to blow the final whistle when out popped his false teeth! As he was picking his false teeth out of the mud, one of the teams scored a goal. The goal was disallowed, and the team lost 3-4!

During the 2010 World Cup, an octopus in a German zoo correctly predicted match results. Flags of the rival teams were painted on two boxes. Food was put in each box. The box that Paul the Octopus chose turned out to be that of the winning team!

Norman Whiteside, from Northern Ireland, was the youngest person to play in World Cup finals. He was only 17 years and 42 days old when he played in 1982.

The first World Cup trophy was called the Jules Rimet Trophy in honour of the Frenchman who had organised the competition. During World War II it was kept hidden in a shoe box under a bed for safe-keeping! In 1983, the trophy was stolen and has never been seen since. The trophy used today is called the FIFA World Cup trophy.

The fastest goal scored in a World Cup match was scored by Hakon Sukur from Turkey in 2002. It took him just 11 seconds to put the ball in the back of the South Korean net.

Brazil is the only country to have appeared in all World Cup final stages and has scored more goals than any other country. It is also the only country to have won the World Cup five times. Brazil's most famous player was Pelé. He won three World Cup medals and scored a staggering 1,282 goals in his career. He is regarded by many as the best footballer of all time.

More than three-quarters of all footballs are made in Pakistan.

A footballer runs 10 kilometres on average during a football match.

Italian footballer Giuseppe Meazza had an embarrassing moment during the 1938 World Cup. His football shorts fell down as he was about to take a penalty.

'Some people believe football is a matter of life and death… I can assure you it is much much more important than that', (Bill Shankley, former Liverpool Manager).

The grounds of some clubs have been used for unusual purposes before becoming soccer grounds.

The Aviva Stadium, Dublin

Club	Ground	Previous use
Aston Villa	Villa Park	Amusement park
West Ham	Upton Park	Cabbage patch
Southampton	The Dell	Duck pond
Exeter City	St James' Park	Pig-grazing land
Aberdeen	Pittodrie	Manure heap

1. Look at the soccer timeline. It shows the development of soccer over the past 150 years or so. What do you think are the three most important changes?
2. Skim through the text and list all the countries mentioned.
3. Which of the soccer grounds would you most like to have visited before it became a soccer ground? Which would you have least liked to visit? Why?
4. Choose another sport and make a timeline for it.

Soccer in the playground

1. List the games you play in the playground. Which is your favourite?
2. What is the biggest cause of arguments in your playground?
3. How do you think these arguments can be avoided?

Whose side are you on?

During break time at St Anne's Primary School, some children play soccer in the playground. Other children are getting fed up with their playground being used as a soccer pitch. Here children, teachers and parents give opinions for and against being allowed to play soccer in the playground. At breaktime will you be on the pitch or in the playground?

For:

- Children should be able to enjoy playing soccer with their friends.
- We should have ball games because both girls and boys love them.
- Playing soccer teaches children to co-operate.
- Soccer lets children use their energy and is good exercise.
- Playing soccer wakes children up in the morning and makes them lively.
- Children can practise soccer and become professional soccer players.
- What is the point of learning soccer if you can't play it in the playground?

Against:

- Soccer should only be played in one part of the playground so non-soccer players have space to play.
- You can't get past the children playing soccer.
- Little children are in danger of being hurt, even small children can kick the ball hard.
- My children are ruining their shoes and trousers.
- Soccer balls can smash windows.
- Soccer should be banned because people are horrible to you when they play.

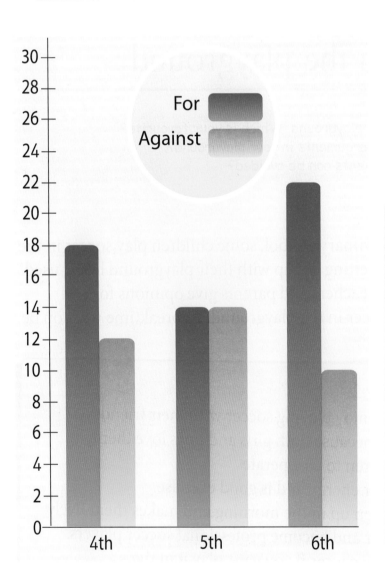

1. Which of the arguments for and against soccer in the playground do you think were made by a.) children b.) adults c.) children and adults. What makes you think this?
2. Look at the chart. Which class has the most children:
   a.) for soccer in the playground?
   b.) against soccer in the playground?
3. Can you think of any other arguments for or against?

1. What do you think a 'sheep-pig' is?
2. Have you ever spent time on a farm?
3. Have you seen the film *Babe* which is based on this story? Tell the class about it.

The Sheep-Pig

Dick King-Smith

Farmer Hogget wins a piglet, called Babe, at a fair. The sheepdog, Fly, looks after Babe and helps him settle in on the farm. Babe is very polite and kind and Ma and the other sheep like him, especially after he helped to rescue them from thieves.

Chapter six: 'Good Pig'

The very next morning Farmer Hogget decided that he would see if the pig would like to come, when he went round the sheep with Fly. I'm daft, he thought, grinning to himself. He did not tell his wife.

Seeing him walk down the yard, crook in hand and hearing him call Fly, Babe was about to settle down for an after-breakfast nap when to his surprise he heard the farmer's voice again.

'Come, Pig,' said Farmer Hogget and to his surprise the pig came.

'I expect it's because of what you did yesterday,' said Fly proudly, as they walked to heel together up the hill. 'The boss must be very pleased with you, dear. You can watch me working.'

When they reached the lower gate, Farmer Hogget opened it and left it open.

'He's going to bring them down into the home paddock, away from the lane,' said Fly quickly. 'You be quiet and keep out of the way,' and she went to sit waiting by the farmer's right side.

'Come by!' he said, and Fly ran left up the slope as the sheep began to bunch above her. Once behind them, she addressed them in her usual way, that is to say sharply.

'Move, fools!' she snapped. 'Down the hill. If you know which way "down" is,' but to her surprise they did not obey. Instead they turned to face her, and some even stamped, and shook their heads at her, while a great chorus of bleating began. ⭐

⭐ Notice Fly's tone of voice. How would you describe it?

To Fly sheep-talk was just so much rubbish, to which she had never paid any attention, but Babe, listening below, could hear clearly what was being said, and although the principal cry was the usual one, there were other voices saying other things. The contrast between the politeness with which they had been treated by yesterday's rescuer and the everlasting rudeness to which they were subjected by this or any wolf brought mutinous thoughts into woolly heads, and words of defiance rang out.  'You got no manners! ...Why can't you ask nicely?... Treat us like muck, you do!' they cried, and one hoarse voice which the pig recognized called loudly, 'We don't want you, wolf. We want Babe!' whereupon they all took it up. 'We want Babe!' they bleated. 'Babe! Babe! Ba-a-a-a-a-be!'

Those behind pushed at those in front, so that they actually edged a pace or two nearer the dog.

For a moment it seemed to Babe that Fly was not going to be able to move them, that she would lose this particular battle of wills; but he had not reckoned with her years of experience. Suddenly quick as a flash, she drove in on them with a growl and with a twisting leap sprang for the nose of the foremost animal; Babe heard the clack of her teeth as the ewe fell over backwards in fright, a fright which immediately ran through all. Defiant no longer, the flock poured down the hill, Fly snapping furiously at their heels, and surged wildly through the gateway. ⭐

'No manners! No manners! No ma-a-a-a-a-anners!' they cried, but an air of panic ran through them as they realized how rebellious they had been. How the wolf

⭐ Do you feel sympathy for the sheep?

⭐ How did Fly regain power over the flock?

would punish them! They ran helter-skelter into the middle of the paddock, and wheeled as one to look back, ears pricked, eyes wide with fear. They puffed and blew, and Ma's hacking cough rang out. But to their surprise they saw that the wolf had dropped by the gateway, and that after a moment the pig came trotting out to one side of them.

Though Farmer Hogget could not know what had caused the near-revolt of the flock, he saw clearly that for some reason they had given Fly a hard time, and that she was angry. It was not like her to gallop sheep in that pell-mell fashion. 'Steady!' he said curtly as she harried the rearguard, and then 'Down!' and 'Stay!' and shut the gate. Shepherding suited Farmer Hogget – there was no waste of words in it.

In the corner of the home paddock nearest to the farm buildings was a smallish fenced yard divided into a number of pens and runways. Here the sheep would be brought at shearing-time or to pick out fat lambs for market or to be treated for various troubles. Farmer Hogget had heard the old ewe cough; he thought he would catch her up and give her another drench. He turned to give an order to Fly lying flat and still behind him, and there, flying flat and still beside her, was the pig.

'Stay, Fly!' said Hogget. And, just for fun, 'Come, Pig!' ⭐

Immediately Babe ran forward and sat at the farmer's right, his front trotters placed neatly together, his big ears cocked for the next command.

Strange thoughts began to stir in Farmer Hogget's mind, and unconsciously he crossed his fingers.

He took a deep breath, and, holding it ... 'Away to me, Pig!' he said softly.

Without a moment's hesitation Babe began the long outrun to the right.

Quite what Farmer Hogget had expected to happen, he could never afterwards clearly remember. What he had not expected was that the pig would run round to the rear of the flock and turn to face it and him, and lie down instantly without a word of further command spoken, just as a well-trained dog would have done. Admittedly, with his jerky little rocking-horse canter he took twice as long to get there as Fly would have, but still, there he was, in the right place, ready and waiting. Admittedly, the sheep had turned to face the pig and were making a great deal of noise, but then Farmer Hogget did not know, and Fly would not listen to, what they were saying. He called the dog to heel, and began to walk with his long loping stride to the collecting-pen in the corner. Out in the middle of the paddock there was a positive babble of talk.

'Good morning!' said Babe. 'I do hope I find you all well, and not too distressed by yesterday's experience?' and immediately it seemed that every sheep had something to say to him.

'Bless his heart!' they cried, and, 'Dear little soul!' and, 'Hullo, Babe!' and, 'Nice to see you again!' and then there was a rasping cough and the sound of Ma's hoarse tones.

'What's up then, young un?' She croaked. 'What be you doing here instead of that wolf?'

Although Babe wanted, literally, to keep on the right side of the sheep, his loyalty to his foster-mother made him say in a rather hurt voice, 'She's not a wolf. She's a sheep-dog.'

'Oh all right then,' said Ma, 'sheep-dog, if you must have it. What dost want, then?'

Babe looked at the army of long sad faces.

'I want to be a sheep-pig,' he said.

'Ha ha!' bleated a big lamb standing next to Ma. 'Ha ha ha-a-a-a!'

'Bide quiet!' said Ma sharply, swinging her head to give the lamb a thumping butt in the side. 'That ain't nothing to laugh at.'

> ⭐ Why does the author say 'just for fun'?

Raising her voice, she addressed the flock.

'Listen to me, all you ewes,' she said, 'and lambs too. This young chap was kind to me, like I told you, when I were poorly. And I told him, if he was to ask me to go somewhere or do something, politely, like he would, why, I'd be only too delighted. We ain't stupid, I told him, all we do want is to be treated right, and we'm as bright as the next beast, we are.'

'We are!' chorused the flock. 'We are! We are! We a-a-a-a-a-are!'

'Right then,' said Ma. 'What shall us do, Babe?'

Babe looked across towards Farmer Hogget, who had opened the gate of the collecting-pen and now stood leaning on his crook, Fly at his feet. The pen was in the left bottom corner of the paddock, and so Babe expected, and at that moment got, the command 'Come by, Pig!' to send him left and so behind the sheep and thus turn them down towards the corner.

He cleared his throat. 'If I might ask a great favour of you,' he said hurriedly, 'could you all please be kind enough to walk down to that gate where the farmer is standing, and to go through it? Take your time, please, there's absolutely no rush.'

A look of pure contentment passed over the faces of the flock, and with one accord they turned and walked across the paddock, Babe a few paces in their rear.

Sedately they walked, and steadily, over to the corner, through the gate, into the pen, and then stood quietly waiting. No one broke ranks or tried to slip away, no one pushed or shoved, there was no noise or fuss. From the oldest to the youngest, they went in like lambs.

Then at last a gentle murmur broke out as everyone in different ways quietly expressed their pleasure.

'Babe!' said Fly to the pig. 'That was quite beautifully done, dear!'

'Thank you so much!' said Babe to the sheep. 'You did that so nicely.'

'Ta!' said the sheep. 'Ta! Ta! Ta-a-a-a-a-a! 'Tis a pleasure to work for such a little gennulman!' And Ma added, 'You'll make a wunnerful sheep-pig, young un, or my name's not Ma-a-a-a-a.'

As for Farmer Hogget, he heard none of this, so wrapped up was he in his own thoughts. He's as good as a dog, he told himself excitedly, he's better than a dog, than any dog! I wonder...!

'Good Pig,' he said.

Then he uncrossed his fingers and closed the gate.

> ☆ Why did the sheep feel so content?

1. What nickname did the sheep have for Fly?
2. What did Fly think of sheep-talk?

3. Fly speaks in a different tone of voice to Babe than she does to the sheep. Find examples.
4. Farmer Hogget does not waste words when speaking to the animals. Find examples of this in the text.
5. Ma talks with a particular English accent. Can you find examples?
6. What impressions of life on a sheep farm do you have from this extract?

7. Why were the sheep defiant towards Fly today?
8. Do you think the animals are happy on the farm?
9. How do we know the sheep like Pig?
10. What kind of character is Farmer Hogget?
11. Do you think the author creates convincing animal dialogue? Give some examples.

12. Do you have a dog? Tell the class about it.

The Sheep

Seumas O'Sullivan

Slowly they pass
In the grey of the evening
Over the wet road,
A flock of sheep.
Slowly they wend
In the grey of the gloaming
Over the wet road
That winds through the town.
Slowly they pass,
And gleaming whitely
Vanish away
In the grey of the evening.

Picture puzzles

1. Do you know any riddles? Share them with the class.
2. Solve these riddles with the help of the picture.

My face is pale, and full and fair;
And round it beauty spots there are;
By day, indeed, I seem less bright,
I'm only seen sometimes at night.
And when the sun has gone to bed
I then begin to show my head.

What is it?
Has a mouth and does not speak,
Has a bed and does not sleep.

What is it? It stands on one leg
With its heart in its head.

I sleep by day, I fly by night.
I have no feathers
To aid my flight.

My tail is long, my coat is brown,
I like the country, I like the town.
I can live in a house or live in a shed,
And I come out to play when you are in bed.

Flip flop fleezy,
When it is in, it is easy.
But when it is out,
It flops all about.
Flip flop fleezy.

It has four legs and a foot
And can't walk.
It has a head
And can't talk.

My first is in ocean but never in sea.
My second's in wasp but never in bee.
My third is in glider and also in flight.
My whole is a creature that comes out at night.

I prefer a bed of lettuce to any other kind,
And frolicking about is most often
on my mind.
My ears are long, and short my tail.
If you try to catch me, you will fail.

44

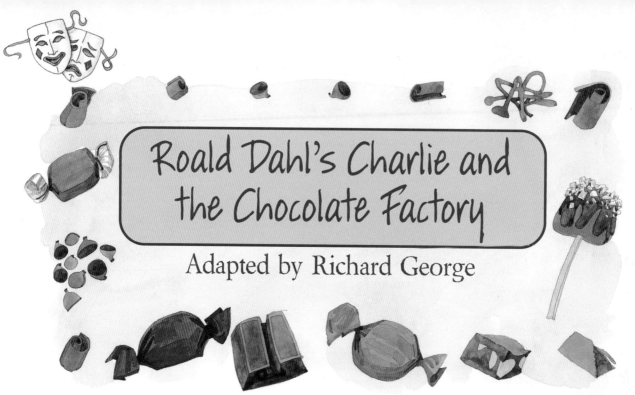

Roald Dahl's Charlie and the Chocolate Factory

Adapted by Richard George

Scene seven

The Invention Room. It is filled with stoves and pipes, pots and kettles, and many strange machines. All enter as scene opens.

Cast
Willy Wonka
Charlie
Mrs Beauregarde
Mr Salt
Violet Beauregarde
Mike Teavee
Ooompa-Loompas
Veruca Salt

Willy   This is the most important room in the entire factory! All my most secret new inventions are cooking and simmering in here! Old Fickelgruber would give his front teeth to be allowed inside, just for three minutes! So would Prodnose and Slugworth and all the other rotten chocolate makers! But now, listen to me! I want no messing about when you go in! No touching! No meddling! And *no tasting*! Is that agreed?

Children   Yes, yes! We won't touch a thing!

Everyone looks around in amazement. Willy Wonka runs around and jumps in excitement from place to place. He approaches and gazes into a machine.

Willy   Everlasting Gobstoppers! They're completely new! I am inventing them for children who are given very little pocket money. You can put an Everlasting Gobstopper in your mouth and you can suck it and suck it and suck it and suck it and suck it… it will never get any smaller!

Violet	It's like gum!
Willy	It is not like gum! Gum is for chewing, and if you tried chewing one of these Gobstoppers here, you'd break your teeth off. But they *taste* terrific! And they change colour once a week! Now that machine over there makes hair toffee but it's not quite perfected yet. But I'll get the mixture right soon! And when I do, then there'll be no excuse any more for little boys and girls going about with bald heads!
Mike	But Mr Wonka, little boys and girls never go about with –
Willy	Don't argue, my dear child… *please* don't argue! Now over here, if you will all step this way, I will show you something I am *terrifically* proud of. Oh, do be careful! Stand back!

He stops at centre stage in front of the Great Gum Machine.

Willy	Here we go!

He begins pushing buttons, and all kinds of noises and lights occur. Finally a small strip of grey cardboard appears from side of machine.

Mike	You mean that's all?
Willy	(*proudly*) That's all! Don't you know what it is?
Violet	(*yelling*) By gum, it's *gum*!!! It's a stick of chewing gum!
Willy	Right you are! (*slapping Violet hard on the back*) It's a stick of the most amazing and fabulous and sensational gum in the world! This gum is a fantastic gum – in that it's a chewing-gum meal! It's a whole three-course dinner all by itself! When I start selling this gum in the shops, it will change everything. It will be the *end* of cooking, marketing, forks, plates, washing up, and garbage! This piece of gum I've just made happens to be tomato soup, roast beef, *and* blueberry pie! But you can have almost anything you want!
Violet	What do you mean by that?
Willy	If you were to start chewing it, you would actually taste *all* of those things. *And* it fills you up! It satisfies you! It's terrific!
Veruca	It's utterly impossible!

Violet   Just so long as it's gum, and I can chew it… then that's for me! (*taking her own piece out of her mouth and sticking it behind her left ear*) Come on, Mr Wonka, hand over this magic gum of yours … and we'll see if the thing works!

Mrs Beau.   Now, Violet… let's not do anything silly.

Violet   I want the gum! What's so silly?

Willy   I would rather you didn't take it. You see, I haven't got it quite right yet. There are still one or two things –

Violet   (*interrupting*) Oh, to heck with that!

She grabs the gum and pops it into her mouth.

Willy   Don't!

Violet   Fabulous! It's great!

Willy   Spit it out!

Mrs Beau.   Keep chewing, kiddo! Keep right on chewing, baby! This is a great day for the Beauregardes! Our little girl is the first person in the world to have a chewing-gum meal!

Willy   (*wringing his hands*) No – no – no – no – no! It isn't ready for eating! It isn't right! You mustn't do it!

Mrs Beau.   Good heavens, girl! What's happening to your nose? It's turning *blue*!

48

Violet   Oh, be quiet, mother, and let me finish!

Mrs Beau.   Your cheeks! Your chin! Your whole face is turning *blue*! Mercy save us! The girl's going blue and purple all over! Violet, you're turning violet, Violet! What is happening to you? You're glowing all over! The whole room is glowing!

Blue lights on only.

Willy   (*sighing and shaking head sadly*) I *told* you I hadn't got it quite right. It always goes wrong when we come to the dessert. It's the blueberry pie that does it. But I'll get it right one day, you wait and see!

Mrs Beau.   Violet … you're swelling up!

Violet begins backing off stage.

Violet   I feel most peculiar!

Violet now disappears off stage.

Mrs Beau.   You're swelling up! You're *blowing up like a balloon*!

Willy   Like a *blueberry*!

Mrs Beau.   Call a doctor!

Mr Salt   Prick her with a pin!

Mrs Beau.   (*wringing her hands helplessly*) Save her!

Willy   It always happens like this. All the Oompa-Loompas that tried it finished up as blueberries. It's most annoying. I just *can't* understand it.

Mrs Beau.   But I don't *want* a blueberry for a daughter! Put her back this instant!

Willy   Tell the Oompa-Loompas over there to roll Miss Beauregarde into the Juicing Room at once!

Mrs Beau.   The *Juicing Room*? What for?

| **Willy** | To *squeeze* her! We've got to squeeze the juice out of her immediately. After that, we'll just have to see how she comes out. But *don't* worry. We'll get her repaired if it's the *last thing we do*. I am sorry about it all … I really am … |

Mrs Beauregarde walks off following Violet.

| **Charlie** | Mr Wonka? Will Violet ever be all right again? |

| **Willy** | She'll come out of the de-juicing machine just as thin as a whistle – and she'll still be purple. Purple from head to toe! But there you are! That's what comes from chewing disgusting gum all day long! |

| **Mike** | If it's so *disgusting*, then why do you make it in your factory? |

| **Willy** | I can't hear a word you're saying. Come on! Off we go! Follow me! |

All exit.

| **Oompa-Loompas** | Dear friends, we surely all agree
There's almost nothing worse to see
Than some repulsive little bum
Who's always chewing chewing gum.
This sticky habit's bound to send
The chewer to a sticky end.
Did any of you ever know
A person called Miss Bigelow? |

This dreadful woman saw no wrong
In chewing, chewing all day long.
And when she couldn't find her gum,
She'd chew up the linoleum,
Or anything that happened near –
A pair of boots, the postman's ear,
Or other people's underclothes,
And once she chewed her boyfriend's nose.
For years and years she chewed away,
Consuming fifty packs a day,
Until one summer's eve, alas,
a horrid business came to pass.
Miss Bigelow went late to bed,
For half an hour she lay and read,
At last, she put her gum away
Upon a special little tray,
And settled back and went to sleep –
(she managed this by counting sheep).
But now, how strange! Although she slept,
Those massive jaws of hers kept
On chewing, chewing through the night,
Even with nothing there to bite.
This sleeping woman's great big trap
Opening and shutting, snap-snap-snap!
Faster and faster, chop-chop-chop,
The noise went on, it wouldn't stop.
Until at last her jaws decide
To pause and open extra wide,
And with the most tremendous chew
They bit the lady's tongue in two.
And that is why we'll try so hard
To save Miss Violet Beaugarde
From suffering an equal fate.
She's still quite young. It's not too late,
Provided she survives the cure.
We hope she does. We can't be sure.

Chocolate

1. Do you like chocolate? What is your favourite kind?
2. In pairs, think of as many words as you can to describe chocolate.
3. Make a list of the many different ways you can enjoy chocolate.

Everybody loves chocolate ... its sweet, delicious flavour leaves a lovely taste in the mouth. The story of chocolate goes back many hundreds of years. The first people to use chocolate were the Aztecs and Mayans who lived in Mexico over a thousand years ago – and they used it as a drink. In the jungles of Mexico grew the cocoa tree. This tree produced large pods as fruit and in these pods were the

seeds that were used to make chocolate. When the Mayans and Aztecs cut down the seeds they ground them and added chilli and other spices to make a bitter drink. In fact the word 'chocolate' comes from the Aztec word *xocolati* that means 'bitter water'. It was not until many hundreds of years later that sugar was added to the chocolate to sweeten it. As well as drinking chocolate, the Aztecs used cocoa beans as money – 100 cocoa beans could buy a slave and 10 beans could buy a rabbit. They also gave the beans as an offering to the gods.

Chocolate was brought to Europe about 500 years ago by Spanish explorers who

A chocolate house in 18th century London

had sailed to the New World. They were given some to drink by the Aztecs – and they liked the taste. Back in Spain, chocolate became a very expensive drink that could be afforded only by the very wealthy. Saucers were invented to keep chocolate from spilling over on to rich people's clothes! It was in Spain that sugar was first added to the chocolate to sweeten it. Soon chocolate houses were opened where people could meet friends and have a chat – a bit like coffee shops today. The first chocolate bars were made about 150 years ago and people have been eating chocolate ever since.

Drinking chocolate

Did you know?

The world's largest chocolate bar weighed 3,580kg. That is as heavy as about 50 adults. It was made in Italy in 2001.

The Aztec emperor is said to have drunk 50 cups of chocolate a day from a gold goblet.

Most cocoa farms today are on the west coast of Africa. The Ivory Coast alone produces 2/5 of the world's cocoa beans. Most of the farms are small and family owned. Between 40 and 50 million people in the world today depend on cocoa for their living. In 2000, some of the chocolate companies set up the World Cocoa Foundation to make sure that cocoa farmers were treated fairly.

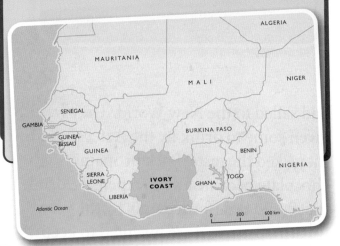

During World War II soldiers were given chocolate every day as part of their rations.

There is a lot of competition today among the many chocolate-making companies. This is sometimes referred to as the chocolate wars.

The most expensive boxes of chocolates in the world are sold at Harrods in London. Each box contains 49 sweets that are wrapped in leather and silk. Each chocolate is decorated with gold – and the cost? A mere £5,000 (about €6,000).

How chocolate is made

1. Cocoa trees need to be between three and five years old before they produce the pods that contain the precious cocoa seeds. The pods grow all along the tree trunk and branches.

2. Farmers use machetes (sharp knives) to cut down the pods and slice open the seeds.

3. The beans are left out under the sun to dry.

4. The beans are packed and sent by ship to the factory.

5. In the factory the seeds are roasted and then ground to make a thick paste.

6. To make chocolate of the paste other things are added next, including milk and sugar.

7. The chocolate is quite thick at this stage, so it is put through giant steam rollers to smooth out the mixture.

8. The chocolate is now poured into moulds to make different-shaped chocolate products.

Chocolate krispies recipe

You will need:

- 100 grams of milk chocolate
- rice krispies
- Paper cake cases

What to do:

1. Break the chocolate into a bowl.
2. Put the bowl over a pan of hot water. (Make sure an adult is with you.)
3. Leave the chocolate to melt, stirring a few times.
4. Pour the rice krispies into the bowl. Mix them in well with the chocolate.
5. Pour the mixture into the paper cake cases.
6. Put the chocolate krispies into the fridge to harden.
7. For a healthier recipe, add raisins to the rice krispies.

1. Who were the first people to use chocolate?
2. Who brought chocolate to Europe for the first time?
3. Talk about the three most interesting facts you have learned about chocolate.
4. Do you know any other chocolate recipes? Talk about them.
5. Design your own wrapper for a new chocolate bar. Give it an exciting name.
6. Would you like to work on a cocoa farm? Why?

Chocolate Cake

Michael Rosen

I love chocolate cake.
And when I was a boy
I loved it even more.

Sometimes we used to have it for tea and Mum used to
say,
'If there's any left over
you can have it to take to school
tomorrow to have at playtime.'
And the next day I would take it to school
wrapped up in tin foil
open it up at playtime
and sit in the corner of the playground
eating it,
you know how the icing on top
is all shiny and it cracks as you
bite into it,
and there's that other kind of icing in
the middle
and it sticks to your hands and you
can lick your fingers
and lick your lips
oh it's lovely.
yeah.

Anyway,
once we had this chocolate cake for tea
and later I went to bed
but while I was in bed
I found myself waking up

licking my lips
and smiling.
I woke up proper.
'The chocolate cake.'
It was the first thing
I thought of.

I could almost see it
so I thought,
what if I go downstairs
and have a little nibble, yeah?

It was all dark
everyone was in bed
so it must have been really late
but I got out of bed,
crept out of the door

there's always a creaky floorboard, isn't there?

Past Mum and Dad's room,
careful not to tread on bits of broken toys
or bits of Lego
you know what it's like treading on Lego
with your bare feet,

yowwww
shhhhhhh

downstairs
into the kitchen
open the cupboard
and there it is
all shining.

So I take it out of the cupboard
put it on the table
and I see that
there's a few crumbs lying about on the plate,
so I lick my finger and run my finger all over the crumbs
scooping them up
and put them into my mouth.

ooooooommmmmmmmm

nice.

Then
I look again
and on one side where it's been cut,
it's all crumbly.

So I take a knife I think I'll just tidy that up a bit,
cut off the crumbly bits
scoop them all up
and into the mouth

oooooommm mmmm

nice.

Look at the cake again.

That looks a bit funny now,
one side doesn't match the other
I'll just even it up a bit, eh?

Take the knife
and slice.
This time the knife makes a little cracky noise
as it goes through that hard icing on top.

59

A whole slice this time,
and into the mouth.

Oh the icing on top
and the icing in the middle
ohhhhhh oooo mmmmmm.

But now
I can't stop myself
Knife –
I just take any old slice at it
and I've got this great big chunk
and I'm cramming it in
what a greedy pig
but it's so nice,

and there's another
and another and I'm squealing and I'm smacking my lips
and I'm stuffing myself with it
and
before I know
I've eaten the lot.
The whole lot.

I look at the plate.
It's all gone.

Oh no
they're bound to notice, aren't they,
a whole chocolate cake doesn't just disappear
does it?

What shall I do?

I know. I'll wash the plate up,
and the knife

and put them away and maybe no one
will notice, eh?

So I do that
and creep creep creep
back to bed
into bed
doze off
licking my lips
with a lovely feeling in my belly.
Mmmmrnmmmmm.

In the morning I get up,
downstairs,
have breakfast,
Mum's saying,
'Have you got your dinner money?'
and I say,
'Yes.'
'And don't forget to take some chocolate cake with you.'
I stopped breathing.

'What's the matter,' she says,
'you normally jump at chocolate cake?'

I'm still not breathing,
and she's looking at me very closely now.

She's looking at me just below my mouth.
'What's that?' she says.
'What's what?' I say.

'What's that there?
'Where?'

'There,' she says, pointing at my chin.
'I don't know,' I say.
'It looks like chocolate,' she says.
'It's not chocolate is it?'
No answer.
'Is it?'
'I don't know.'
She goes to the cupboard
looks in, up, top, middle, bottom,
turns back to me.
'It's gone.
It's gone.
You haven't eaten it, have you?'
'I don't know.'
'You don't know. You don't know if you've eaten a whole
chocolate cake or not?
When? When did you eat it?'

So I told her,

and she said
well what could she say?
'That's the last time I give you any cake to take
to school.
Now go. Get out
no wait
not before you've washed your dirty sticky face.'
I went upstairs
looked in the mirror
and there it was,
just below my mouth,
a chocolate smudge.
The give-away.
Maybe she'll forget about it by next week.

62

Chocs

Carol Ann Duffy

Into the half-pound box of Moonlight
my small hand crept.
There was an electrifying rustle.
There was a dark and glamorous scent.
Into my open, moist mouth
the first Montelimar went.

Down in the crinkly second layer,
five finger-piglets snuffled
among the Hazelnut Whirl,
the Caramel Square,
the Black Cherry and Almond Truffle.

Bliss.

I chomped. I gorged.
I stuffed my face,
till only the Coffee Cream
was left for the owner of the box –
Tough luck, Anne Pope –
oh, and half an Orange Supreme.

Recycling

1. Make a list of the foods that come in these types of container:
   a.) paper   b.) cardboard   c.) polystyrene   d.) aluminium   e.) a mix of these.
2. Why do you think they are packaged in this way?

Have you ever wondered where all the things that are thrown away go?

Think of all the things people sometimes put in the bin in their kitchen: cereal boxes, tea bags, glass jars, eggshells, empty tins, potato skins, newspapers, cartons, and plastic bottles. I'm sure you could list hundreds of things. Most of this rubbish is put into plastic bags or bins and taken away to a dump. But all these things take up a lot of space and some dumps are getting very full. In Ireland, over one million tonnes of waste is sent to landfill each year. That is equal in weight to nearly one million cars. So it is very important that we start to think about rubbish in a different way. It is not all 'waste'. Many things can be used again in some way. This is called recycling. More than three-quarters of our bin waste can be recycled.

What can be recycled?

Glass
Anything made from glass can be recycled. The glass is either cleaned and re-used or smashed and melted to make new glass.

Drink and food cans
Aluminium cans may be recycled. (You know it's made from aluminium if a magnet doesn't stick to it). The ring-pulls can also be recycled.

Cans made from steel, such as baked beans cans, may also be recycled.

Paper
Newspaper, cardboard and other papers can all be recycled.

Plastic
Some plastics can be recycled such as drinks bottles, milk containers and detergent bottles. Did you know that 25 recycled drinks bottles can be used to make an adult's fleece jacket?

Leftovers
Foods such as banana and potato skins, eggshells and cabbage leaves don't have to be thrown in the bin. If you have a garden, they can be used to make a compost heap. Almost one-third of all household waste can be turned into compost. Many gardeners have a corner or a compost bin where they put old grass cuttings, leaves and other leftovers. In time this turns into compost which can be mixed with soil as plant food.

A domestic compost bin

What can't be recycled?
Some things can never be used again and must be dumped, for example, old cans of paint, used batteries and some plastic containers. But some of these can be dangerous to the environment, so care must be taken when disposing of them.

1. List 20 things you might find in a rubbish bin. Which ones:
a.) can be recycled b.) can be put in the compost heap c.) have to go to the dump?

Glass recycling loop

(1) We bring our empty glass bottles and jars to the bottle bank where we sort them by colour.

(2) The glass is taken by lorry to the recycling plant.

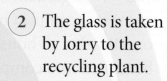

(5) The glass cullet is taken to a processing plant where it is melted down and remade into new glass bottles and jars.

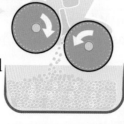

(4) The glass is crushed into small pieces called glass cullet.

(3) The glass is cleaned and labels and lids are removed.

66

How do you start recycling?

At home:
Ask your family to start sorting the rubbish. For example, you could have a box for glass bottles and jars. When it is full, take it to the nearest bottle bank for recycling. The same could be done with old newspapers. If you have a garden you could ask someone to help you start a compost heap. You will then be sending a much smaller amount of rubbish to the dump every week and helping the environment.

At school:
Green Schools is an international programme that is run in Ireland by An Taisce with the help of Local Authorities. It is an education programme and it encourages the whole school to work towards a better environment. Successful schools are awarded a Green Flag.

To find out more, look up: www.greenschoolsireland.org

Recycling

If you see this symbol printed on packaging it means it has been made from recycled material.
Remember recycling is a loop that works only if the collected materials are recycled, bought and used again. It is important to look out for products that have the recycling symbol.

The Newcomer

Brian Patten

'There's something new in the river,'
The fish said as it swam,
'It's got no scales, no fins, no gills,
And ignores the impassable dam.'

'There's something new in the trees,'
I heard a bloated thrush sing.
'It's got no beak, no claws, no feathers,
And not even the ghost of a wing.'

'There's something new in the warren!'
The rabbit said to the doe,
'It's got no fur, no eyes, no paws,
Yet digs deeper than we can go.'

'There's something new in the whiteness,'
Said the snow-bright polar-bear,
'I saw its shadow on a glacier,
But it left no foot-prints there.'

Throughout the animal kingdom
The news was spreading fast –

No beak no claws no feathers,
No scales no fur no gills,
It lives in the trees and the water,
In the earth and the snow and the hills,
And it kills and it kills and it kills.

1. Have you seen the film based on the book Charlotte's Web? Talk about it.
2. Look at the pictures. What do you think will happen in this chapter?

Charlotte's Web

E.B. White

Chapter one: Before breakfast

'Where's Papa going with that axe?' said Fern to her mother as they were setting the table for breakfast.

'Out to the hoghouse,' replied Mrs Arable.

'Some pigs were born last night.'

'I don't see why he needs an axe,' continued Fern, who was only eight.

'Well,' said her mother, 'one of the pigs is a runt. It's very small and weak, and it will never amount to anything. So your father has decided to do away with it.'

'Do *away* with it?' shrieked Fern. 'You mean kill it?

Just because it's smaller than the others?'

Mrs Arable put a pitcher of cream on the table.

'Don't yell, Fern!' she said. 'Your father is right. The pig would probably die anyway.'

Fern pushed a chair out of the way, and ran outdoors. The grass was wet and the earth smelled of springtime. Fern's sneakers were sopping by the time she caught up with her father.

'Please don't kill it!' she sobbed. 'It's unfair.'

Mr Arable stopped walking.

'Fern,' he said gently, 'you will have to learn to control yourself.'

'Control myself?' yelled Fern. 'This is a matter of life and death, and you talk about *controlling* myself.' Tears ran down her cheeks and she took hold of the axe and tried to pull it out of her father's hand.

'Fern,' said Mr Arable, 'I know more about raising a litter of pigs than you do. A weakling makes trouble. Now run along!'

'But it's unfair,' cried Fern. 'The pig couldn't help being born small, could it? If *I* had been very small at birth, would you have killed *me*?'

What are your first impressions of Fern?

Mr Arable smiled. 'Certainly not,' he said, looking down at his daughter with love. 'But this is different. A little girl is one thing, a little runty pig is another.'

'I see no difference,' replied Fern, still hanging on to the axe. 'This is the most terrible case of injustice I ever heard of.'

A queer look came over John Arable's face. He seemed almost ready to cry himself. ⭐

'All right,' he said. 'You go back to the house and I will bring the runt when I come in. I'll let you raise it on a bottle, like a baby. Then you'll see what trouble a pig can be.'

When Mr Arable returned to the house half an hour later, he carried a carton under his arm. Fern was upstairs changing her sneakers. The kitchen table was set for breakfast, and the room smelt of coffee, bacon, damp plaster, and wood-smoke from the stove.

'Put it on her chair!' said Mrs Arable. Mr Arable set the carton down at Fern's place. Then he walked to the sink and washed his hands and dried them on the roller towel.

Fern came slowly down the stairs. Her eyes were red from crying. As she approached her chair, the carton wobbled, and there was a scratching noise. Fern looked at her father. Then she lifted the lid of the carton. There, inside, looking up at her, was the newborn pig. It was a white one. The morning light shone through its ears, turning them pink.

⭐ **What do you imagine John Arable is thinking?**

70

'He's yours,' said Mr Arable. 'Saved from an untimely death. And may the good Lord forgive me for this foolishness.'

Fern couldn't take her eyes off the tiny pig. 'Oh,' she whispered. 'Oh, look at him! He's absolutely perfect.'

She closed the carton carefully. First she kissed her father then she kissed her mother. Then she opened the lid again, lifted the pig out, and held it against her cheek. At this moment her brother Avery came into the room. Avery was ten. He was heavily armed – an air rifle in one hand, a wooden dagger in the other. 'What's that?' he demanded. 'What's Fern got?'

'She's got a guest for breakfast,' said Mrs Arable. 'Wash your hands and face, Avery!'

'Let's see it!' said Avery, setting his gun down. 'You call that miserable thing a pig? That's a fine specimen of a pig – it's no bigger than a white rat.'

'Wash up and eat your breakfast, Avery!' said his mother. 'The school bus will be along in half an hour.'

'Can I have a pig too, Pop?' asked Avery.

'No, I only distribute pigs to early risers,' said Mr Arable. 'Fern was up at daylight, trying to rid the world of injustice. As a result, she now has a pig. A small one, to be sure, but nevertheless a pig. It just shows what can happen if a person gets out of bed promptly. Let's eat!'

But Fern couldn't eat until her pig had had a drink of milk. Mrs Arable found a baby's nursing bottle and a rubber nipple. She poured warm milk into the bottle, fitted the nipple over the top, and handed it to Fern. 'Give him his breakfast!' she said.

⭐ How are Fern and Avery different?

A minute later, Fern was seated on the floor in the corner of the kitchen with her infant between her knees, teaching it to suck from the bottle. The pig, although tiny, had a good appetite and caught on quickly.

The school bus honked from the road.

'Run!' commanded Mrs Arable, taking the pig from Fern and slipping a doughnut into her hand. Avery grabbed his gun and another doughnut.

The children ran out to the road and climbed into the bus. Fern took no notice of the others in the bus. She just sat and stared out of the window, thinking what a blissful world it was and how lucky she was to have entire charge of a pig. By the time the bus reached school, Fern had named her pet, selecting the most beautiful name she could think of.

'Its name is Wilbur,' she whispered to herself.

She was still thinking about the pig when the teacher said: 'Fern, what is the capital of Pennsylvania?'

'Wilbur,' replied Fern, dreamily. The pupils giggled. Fern blushed.

---

1. Why did Fern's dad decide to do away with the small pig?
2. Did Fern eat her breakfast that morning? Why?

3. Charlotte's Web is set in America. Find words in the story that show this.
4. What tactics does Fern use to try to save the pig?

5. How do you think Fern gets on with her father?
6. If Fern's Dad had killed the runt of the litter, how would the story be different?
7. How does the author grab your attention right from the start of this extract?
8. Look up the word 'arable' in the dictionary. Why do you think the author gave the family this name?
9. Fern's mother plays a small but important part in this extract. Do you agree?
10. Do you think Fern will get tired of the pig after a while?

11. Fern felt strongly about giving the little pig a chance. What have you ever felt strongly about? Tell the class about it.
12. Find the capital city of Pennsylvania. How many other capital cities do you know?

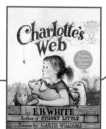

72

Good Company

Leonard Clark

I sleep in a room at the top of the house
With a flea, and a fly, and a soft-scratching mouse,
And a spider that hangs by a thread from the ceiling,
Who gives me each day such a curious feeling
When I watch him at work on the beautiful weave
Of his web that's so fine I can hardly believe
It won't all end up in such terrible tangles,
For he sways as he weaves, and spins as he dangles.
I cannot get up to that spider, I know,
And I hope he won't get down to me here below,
And yet, when I wake in the chill morning air
I'd miss him if he were not still swinging there,
For I have in my room such good company,
There's him, and the mouse, and the fly, and the flea.

73

Spiders

1. Do you like spiders? Why?
2. What do spiders eat? How do you think they catch their prey?

Types of spiders

There are over 30,000 different kinds of spider, and they can be found all over the world. They are able to survive in hot and cold climates, in deserts, rainforests and grasslands. One species, the diving bell spider, can even live underwater! The Arctic Circle, the Antarctic and the deepest oceans are the only places where spiders are not found. Spiders are very useful to humans because they eat insects, which help to keep their numbers under control. Only a small number (about 25) are harmful to humans.

Arachnid or insect?

	Legs	Antennae	Wings	Poisonous bite or sting	Eats plants	Eats other animals
Insect	6	2	Most have 2 or 4	Some	Some	Some
Arachnid	8	None	None	Nearly all	None	All

All spiders:
- have eight legs
- have large jaws and sharp fangs to bite prey
- have spinnerets that spin silk for making webs
- are divided into two body parts; the head and thorax, and the abdomen

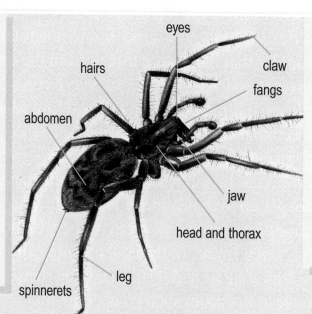

Most spiders:
- have eight eyes, but many cannot see very well
- have hairs on their legs that can sense the movement of other animals nearby
- have fangs through which they can inject poison into their prey

It is often thought that spiders are insects, but they are in fact a different kind of animal called an arachnid. There are important differences between the two. Typical insects include ants, bees, beetles and butterflies. Typical arachnids include spiders, scorpions and ticks. All spiders are carnivores. They bite their prey, then most of them inject a poison that kills or paralyses their victims, making them ready to eat. Each type of spider catches its prey in its own special way. Some ambush their prey, lying in wait until it comes near enough to attack. Some are hunters and move around actively looking for prey. Others spin webs from silk to help them trap their prey.

Life cycle of a garden spider

Most spiders live for about a year but some can live for up to 20 years. This chart shows the life cycle of a garden spider.

1. In autumn, the adult female spider spins a little silk bag, called an egg sac or cocoon. In it she lays over 800 eggs. She then seals the sac with more silk to protect the eggs.

2. The adult female stays with the cocoon until she dies when the weather gets very cold.

3. During winter, the baby spiders begin to hatch inside the sac where they are safe. Baby spiders are called spiderlings and are pale yellow in colour.

4. In spring, as they begin to grow, they chew their way out of the sac. They stay close to each other for a few days only.

5. After spinning a long silk thread, the spiderling waits for the wind to catch it. It floats on it and is blown to a new home. This is known as ballooning.

6. Throughout the summer, the spiderling spins a sticky silken web, in order to trap insects for food.

7. Before the spiderling is fully grown, it will shed its skin up to five times. This is known as moulting.

1. Is a spider an insect? How do you know?
2. List words in the text that are linked to spiders.
3. How many different kinds of spider can you name? Choose one and find out as much as you can about it.

The Vikings

1. When did the Vikings first come to Ireland? Skim through the unit to find dates.
2. Look at the headings. What do you expect to learn about the Vikings?

Raiders

About 1,200 years ago, people called the Vikings lived in Norway, Sweden and Denmark. They were also known as the Norsemen (Northmen) because they came from the north of Europe. They were great travellers and brave warriors. The Vikings had very fast ships called longboats that could travel great distances. Some Vikings travelled as far as Russia and Greenland.

The Viking warship

The Viking warship was the longest, narrowest and speediest of the Viking boats. It could sail up shallow inlets and land quickly to make a surprise attack.

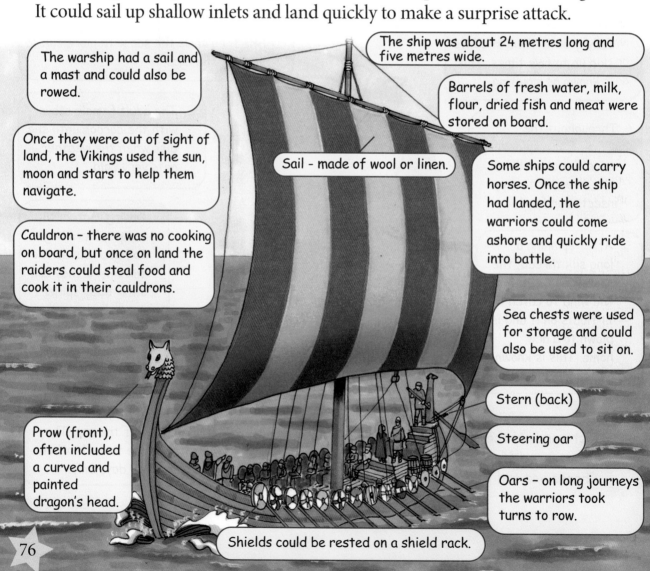

The warship had a sail and a mast and could also be rowed.

The ship was about 24 metres long and five metres wide.

Once they were out of sight of land, the Vikings used the sun, moon and stars to help them navigate.

Barrels of fresh water, milk, flour, dried fish and meat were stored on board.

Sail - made of wool or linen.

Some ships could carry horses. Once the ship had landed, the warriors could come ashore and quickly ride into battle.

Cauldron – there was no cooking on board, but once on land the raiders could steal food and cook it in their cauldrons.

Sea chests were used for storage and could also be used to sit on.

Prow (front), often included a curved and painted dragon's head.

Stern (back)

Steering oar

Oars – on long journeys the warriors took turns to row.

Shields could be rested on a shield rack.

The Viking warrior

The word 'viking' means raider or pirate and the Vikings attacked towns and villages around the coasts of Europe. They stole cattle, horses, gold and silver. They even took prisoners and sold them as slaves elsewhere.

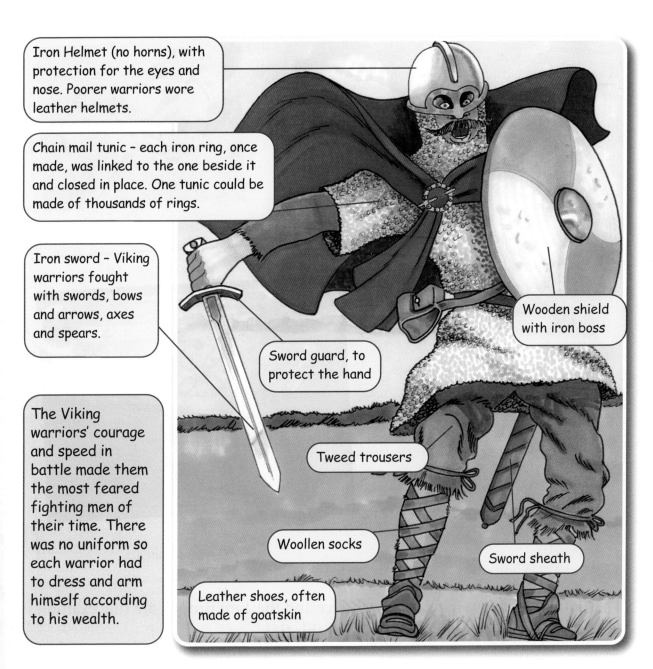

Iron Helmet (no horns), with protection for the eyes and nose. Poorer warriors wore leather helmets.

Chain mail tunic – each iron ring, once made, was linked to the one beside it and closed in place. One tunic could be made of thousands of rings.

Iron sword – Viking warriors fought with swords, bows and arrows, axes and spears.

Sword guard, to protect the hand

Wooden shield with iron boss

The Viking warriors' courage and speed in battle made them the most feared fighting men of their time. There was no uniform so each warrior had to dress and arm himself according to his wealth.

Tweed trousers

Woollen socks

Sword sheath

Leather shoes, often made of goatskin

The Vikings in Ireland

At this time Ireland was a rich country. Irish monasteries were famous for their learning and wealth. In 791, the Vikings raided Ireland for the first time. They attacked the monastery on Lambay Island near Dublin. After that they attacked many other monasteries around the country.

The Tara Brooch

The Book of Durrow

The Ardagh Chalice

The Book of Durrow, the Ardagh Chalice and the Tara Brooch are fine examples of the treasures to be found in Ireland at this time.

Round Towers

Many monasteries built tall stone towers which could have been used as lookout towers and as places to keep both people and precious treasure safe. The door to each tower was three metres above the ground and was reached by a ladder, which could be pulled up once the last person was safely inside.

Dublin

In 841, the Vikings built a fort for their longboats at the mouth of the River Liffey. This fort grew into the town of Dublin. The word 'Dublin' means 'black pool' (*Dubh Linn*). The name comes from the deep pool at the mouth of the Liffey where the Vikings anchored their ships. The Vikings were great traders and Dublin became one of the main trading cities in Europe. Wine, furs, silks and pottery were brought to Dublin. In return, the Vikings traded fish, timber, iron and leather. Dublin wasn't the only fort built by the Vikings. These settlements, called longphorts, became Ireland's first towns and cities. Dublin, Wexford, Cork and Waterford began as longphorts.

The defeat of the Vikings

Even though Dublin became an important trading city, the Vikings continued raiding monasteries and towns around Ireland. On Good Friday, 1014, there was a great battle between the Irish and the Vikings at Clontarf, near Dublin. The Irish were led by Brian Boru, the High King of Ireland. The Irish won the battle and many of the Vikings were killed. But Brian Boru was also killed. After the battle, many Vikings still lived in Dublin and continued trading as they had before. But they were no longer as powerful.

1. Look at the drawing of a Viking warship. What do you think life on board the ship was like?
2. Look at a map of Ireland. Find the towns and cities founded by the Vikings.
3. Choose one of the Irish treasures mentioned in the text. Find out as much as you can about it.
4. Imagine you lived in Ireland when the Vikings invaded. Tell about a Viking raid you experienced. Include details such as: what it was like/how you felt/how you escaped.

Viking Dublin

The city of Dublin was small, crowded and smelly. People lived very close together and many of them kept sheep, goats and geese.

The Vikings were the first people to use money in Ireland. These are Viking coins that were found in Dublin in 1981.

Women wore long linen or woollen dresses, woollen socks and leather shoes. In the winter, they wore fur hats and cloaks.

A tanner making leather

A merchant selling slaves

Salted meat and fish were left hanging out to dry. In this way, the Vikings had food all year round.

An Arab trader selling silk and glass

Wooden paths

The wooden wall protected ships from attack.

A shipbuilder at work. The words **keel** and **starboard** were brought into English language by the Vikings.

Harbour

Women spent much of their time spinning and weaving blankets and clothes.

Viking houses were very small. Most houses only had three rooms. The houses were made from twigs, straw and mud. They had thatched roofs.

When Vikings went raiding they wore helmets and padded leather jackets. Sometimes their jackets were lined with bones to make them stronger.

A smith working in his forge

A slave carrying wine home

1. Compare Viking clothing and houses with clothes and houses today. How are they alike? How are they different?
2. How do you think people traded before the Vikings introduced coins into Ireland?
3. The Vikings left their own countries because of the harshness of life there. Find out about what life might have been like for them.

Sailing

David English

Consider the Viking keel
Cutting keen,
Slicing over the green deep.

Hear the hiss of the salt foam
Curling off at the bow,
And the wake closing quietly
In bubbles behind.

Listen to the sound of the
    thumping drum,
See the helmets shine in the sun.
Feel, with your finger,
The full sail drawn tight
As they drive home before
    the wind.

The Gold Cross of Killadoo

John Quinn

Chapter one: The Raid

At last the great tower of Killadoo loomed before them. Derval scrambled over the boundary wall and staggered up to the base of the tower. 'There! I win! I win!' She had scarcely enough breath to announce her victory. Eoin half-fell over the wall and collapsed at his sister's feet.

'Only –' He fought for his breath. 'Only because you tripped me!'

'Did not. You fell yourself!'

'Did so!'

'Did not. Anyway it serves you right! You cheated at the start!'

'No I didn't. I said – '

'Come, you two! Do you ever stop arguing?' The tubby figure of Brother Killian loomed above them, his moonface beaming a warm smile down on the embarrassed pair. Derval struggled to her feet. ⭐

'Oh, hello, Brother Killian. We – We've come to see the cross.'

'Oh, indeed,' Killian giggled. 'I knew you were coming this last while! I could hear the shouting across the fields!'

Derval ignored the monk's remarks. 'Is it ready? Is it finished? Is it?'

⭐ What is your first impression of Derval and Eoin? Why do you think they were embarrassed?

83

'Patience, my friends! Patience!' Killian placed a hand on each
head.

'But we came especially to see the cross,' Eoin pleaded.

'And so you shall!'

'So it *is* finished,' Derval gave a little leap of joy.

'Oh come on, Brother Killian. Where is it?'

'You don't expect me to carry a gold cross in my habit, do you?'

'Well, where is it then?' Derval stamped her foot in annoyance.

'Really, Derval. You are a most impatient girl!'

Derval looked away quickly. 'Well – we've come a long way,' she whispered.

'All right! All right! I've been too hard on you!' Killian put his arms around both
children. 'I'll take you to Brother Cormac. He's polishing the cross before we
place it in the oratory. But first...'

'Ah Brother Killian,' the children chorused.

Killian ignored them. 'But first ... a present for your mother. I promised her
something in return for the broth she sent me last winter when I was not well.'

'Yes, Brother,' Derval sighed, 'but the cross ...'

The monk turned to the boy and stopped. 'Eoin, you have my sympathy. How do you put up with this girl?' he asked with a wink. ⭐

Eoin took the hint. 'Oh, it's a hard life all right!'

Derval muttered fiercely to herself. Killian gave a hearty laugh, his belly heaving beneath his habit. 'Ah, poor Derval. We tease you too much! Come!' Brother Killian led the children down a narrow path into a quiet corner of the settlement. He paused near a group of little mounds and held up his hand. 'Listen! Our friends the bees are busy at work!' The air was heavy with the humming of bees. 'The little bees; they work so hard and then give us the fruits of their work!'

Derval was beginning to lose her patience again when Killian reached into the long grass and offered her something wrapped in cloth. 'Here! A fine pot of honey for your mother. Mind you don't spill it!'

'Mmm!' Eoin mumbled. 'My teeth are watering already.'

'Thanks, Brother Killian,' Derval said. 'Our mother will be very pleased. Now can we see –?'

'Shhh!' Eoin interrupted his sister. 'What's that noise?' The three froze and listened intently. ⭐

'It's just the bees, silly,' Derval said.

'No, child. Listen!' Brother Killian put his hand on the girl's shoulder.

'It's ... It's horses,' Eoin cried, 'and men ... running.'

'You're right, child,' Killian said with anxiety.

'We have visitors! Run, let you! Run! To the tower!'

'Who? What visitors?' Derval was bewildered by the sudden change in the monk's voice.

'Norsemen! Run!' Killian barked.

'But what about you?' Eoin pleaded.

'I'm going to hide the gold cross. That's the sort of thing these "visitors" are interested in. Now go!' Killian pushed the two children in the direction of the tower and, leaving the path, he waded through the long grass towards the chapel.

'No, we'll help you,' Derval said defiantly.

'They'll never suspect us.' ⭐

⭐ Why did Brother Killian say that?

⭐ What do you think was going through their minds?

⭐ Do you agree with Derval? What would you do if you were in her shoes?

'And anyway, we came to see the cross,' Eoin added.

'Stupid children. Don't you realise your lives are in danger?' Killian pleaded. 'These Norsemen ask no questions. They'll ...'

'They'll have to catch us first!' Derval laughed, but a bit nervously. 'We're coming with you, Brother.'

'Oh all right!' Killian shook his head in desperation. 'If the Norsemen don't kill me, your mother will! Come. We must hurry.'

The children followed as Killian waddled towards the little church. Behind them the noise grew louder and warning shouts pierced the air as other monks realised the danger. The bell began to ring again – far more urgently this time.

'Cormac! Cormac! Come quickly. We must hide the cross!' Killian shouted as he burst into the church. It was so dark inside that even with the door open it took a little while for the children to get used to the absence of light. Eventually they were able to distinguish a bent figure huddled before the altar. 'Poor old Cormac!' Killian muttered. 'Too busy to hear anything!' Cormac was humming away to himself as he polished. Even in the poor light the brilliant sheen of the cross took the children's breath away.

'It's so beautiful!' Derval sighed.

'Well we haven't time to stand and admire it now,' Killian urged. 'Come, Cormac. We have visitors – the Norsemen. We must go to the tower.' The old monk clasped the cross to his chest and muttered in whispers.

'Wait!' Eoin cried. 'Look, Brother Killian. You take Brother Cormac to the tower and we'll make a run for it with the cross!'

How does the author create suspense on this page?

'With the cross? You?' Killian's round red face looked as if it would explode.

'Of course!' Derval chirped. 'The Norsemen won't bother with us. We'll wrap the cross in this old cloth and I'll hide it in my cloak.'

'I don't know,' Killian shook his head. 'If anything happened to you – or the cross ...' He watched Cormac shuffle slowly away. 'But then, we might not make it to the tower...' He scratched his head. 'All right! I'll take the chance.' ⭐

Eoin and Derval looked at each other in anticipation. Killian had to wrestle with the old monk as he prised the cross from his grasp while trying to explain his action at the same time. 'Here!'

He handed the cross to Derval.

The look on his face showed that he still was not sure he was doing the right thing.

'Be careful! Go back through the bee-garden. Run!

God protect you! God protect all of us. Go!' He turned to Cormac, who stood at the door of the church with a puzzled look on his face. The children ran away through the tall grass.

'Come, Cormac,' Killian cried. 'I don't think either us would be able for those Norsemen. We must get to the tower!' ⭐

⭐ Do you think Brother Killian was right to take a chance? What would you have done?

⭐ Have your impressions of Derval and Eoin changed since the start of the story? In what way?

1. Why were the children visiting the monk?
2. Where were the monks going to place the gold cross?
3. What gift did Brother Killian have for the children's mother?

4. Scan the text for words related to life as a monk.
5. How do we know that 'the visitors' were not welcome?
6. What can we tell about life on the settlement?
7. Brother Killian is an important character in this story. What kind of person is he?
8. Do you agree with Brother Killian when he said that Derval was impatient? Why?

9. Why do you think Brother Killian suggested that the children escape through the bee garden?
10. Do you think they will succeed in saving the cross? Why do you think this?

11. What do you know about the Norsemen?
12. Have you ever taken a chance? How did it work out?

Hurling and camogie

1. List as many words as you know to do with hurling and camogie.
2. What do the letters GAA stand for?
3. What sports does the GAA promote?

Hurling

Hurling is the oldest Irish sport and very popular. It has been played in Ireland for thousands of years. It is the fastest and one of the most skilful field games in the world.

Men playing hurling

The sport is played using a stick and a small ball. The stick is called a hurley or a *camán* and the ball is called a sliotar. There are fifteen players on a hurling team today. Long ago neighbouring villages played each other in games of hurling. The games went on for hours and even days. Sometimes there were hundreds of players on each team.

Senior inter-county hurling games last for 70 minutes, 35 minutes a half. A hurling pitch can be up to 145 metres long and 90 metres wide. A point is scored when the sliotar goes over the bar. A goal is scored when the sliotar goes between the posts and under the bar and is worth three points. Hurling players wear helmets and shin guards for protection. Helmets are now compulsory.

Camogie

Camogie, played by women, is almost identical to the game of hurling. Camogie was first played in 1904. It is played using a hurley and a sliotar and there are 15 players on a camogie team. A camogie game is played over 60 minutes, 30 minutes a half. A camogie player wears a skirt or a divided skirt and all players, including the goalkeeper, wear the same team colours.

Women playing camogie

Player positions

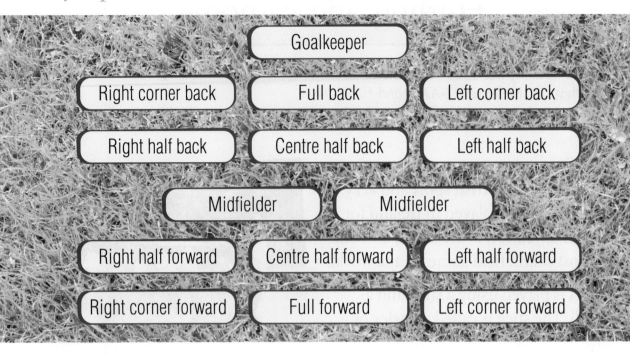

Goalkeeper

Right corner back | Full back | Left corner back

Right half back | Centre half back | Left half back

Midfielder | Midfielder

Right half forward | Centre half forward | Left half forward

Right corner forward | Full forward | Left corner forward

Parts of a hurley

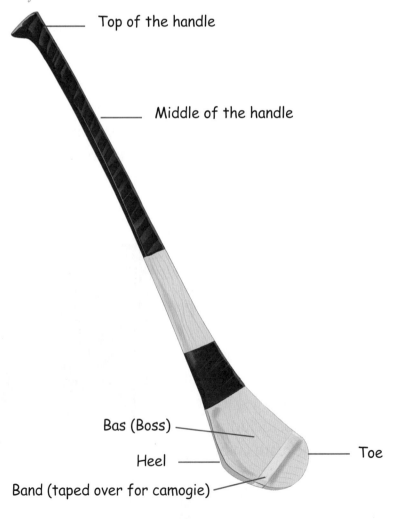

Top of the handle

Middle of the handle

Bas (Boss)

Heel

Band (taped over for camogie)

Toe

Hurleys

The hurley is used to hit and carry the sliotar. A hurley can vary in length from 61cm to 94cm. Hurleys are made from the wood of the ash tree and the game of hurling is also known as 'the clash of the ash'. When the ash tree is about 20 years old, its wood can be used to make hurleys. The wood is sawn into lengths and left to dry for about nine months. Nowadays, most hurleys are made by machine, using a hurley-shaped template. A metal strip is placed around the toe of the bas to stop it splitting. A player can put tape around the handle to give better grip. Man-made materials are also used to make hurleys.

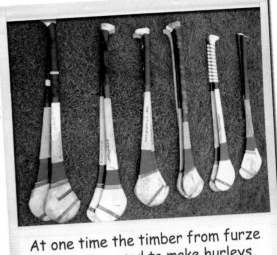
At one time the timber from furze bushes was used to make hurleys.

Sliotars

Sliotars are made from leather or plastic. They come in different sizes. A 'size 4' weighs between 90 grams and 110 grams and measures 21 cm in circumference. This size sliotar is used in camogie. A 'size 5' sliotar weighs between 100 grams and 130 grams and measures between 23 and 25 cm in circumference. This size sliotar is used in hurling.

At one time sliotars were made from horsehair.

Name the sport

Galway is the only county in Connacht ever to have won the Senior Hurling Championship.

In 1942, the first Senior Camogie final was broadcast on radio.

Dublin has won the most All-Ireland Senior Camogie Championship games a record number of 26 times.

The 1939 Senior Hurling final between Cork and Kilkenny has been described as one of the most exciting and most famous hurling matches of all time. It was played during a fierce thunder storm and has become known as the 'Thunder and Lightning final'. The final score was 2–7 to 3–3, with victory going to Kilkenny on 3 September 1939. This was a most important day in Irish sport. It was also the day that World War II began.

Hurling, camogie and football finals are played in Croke Park. The hurling final is normally played on the first Sunday in September. In 1984, the hurling final was played in Semple Stadium in Thurles, Co. Tipperary. This was to celebrate the 100th birthday (centenary) of the founding of the GAA. The GAA was founded on 1 November 1884, in Hayes Hotel, Thurles.

Henry Shefflin from Kilkenny has played in 11 All-Ireland Hurling finals – more than any other hurler. His nickname is King Henry.

In 1990, the Kilkenny and Cork camogie teams flew to New York and staged a replay of the All-Ireland final.

In 1928, Michael Aherne of Cork achieved the highest individual score in a Senior Hurling final. He scored 19 points (5–4) against Galway.

1. Hurling and camogie are very skilful and exciting games. Do you agree with this? Give three reasons to back up your opinion.
2. Make up a hurling quiz based on what you have read and ask the person next to you to answer the questions.
3. Add some more 'Did you Know' facts of your own.
4. Find out in what years Galway won the Senior Hurling final.
5. Find out some interesting facts about the county you support.

The Story of Tracy Beaker

Jacqueline Wilson

Chapter one: My Book About Me

ABOUT ME

My name is	Tracy Beaker	
I am	10 **years**	**2 months old**
My birthday is on	8 May	

It's not fair, because that dopey Peter Ingham has his birthday then too, so we just got the one cake between us. And we had to hold the knife to cut the cake together. Which meant we only had half a wish each. Wishing is for babies anyway. They don't come true. ✩

I was born at _____ some hospital somewhere. I looked cute when I was a little baby but I bet I yelled a lot.

✩ What does this tell us about Tracy?

I am _____ cms tall. I don't know. I've tried measuring with a ruler but it keeps wobbling about and I can't reach properly. I don't want to get any of the other children to help me. This is my private book.

I weigh _____ kgs. I don't know that either. Jenny has got scales in her bathroom but they're stones and pounds. I don't weigh many of them. I'm a little titch.

My eyes are black and I make them go all wicked and witchy. I quite fancy being a witch. I'd make up all these incredibly evil spells and wave my wand and ZAP Louise's golden curls would all fall out and ZAP Peter Ingham's silly squeaky voice would get sillier and squeakier and he'd grow whiskers and a long tail and ZAP ... there's not room on this bit of the page, but I've still got all sorts of ZAPs inside my head.

My hair is fair and very long and curly. I am telling fibs. It's dark and difficult and it sticks up in all the wrong places.

My skin is spotty when I eat a lot of sweets.

Stick a photo of yourself here I'm not really cross-eyed. I was just pulling a silly face.

> What other spells might Tracy cast?

94

I started this book on I don't know. Who cares what the date is? You always have to put the date at school. I got fed up with this and put 2091 in my Day Book and wrote about all these rockets and space ships and monsters legging it down from Mars to eat us all up, as if we'd all whizzed one hundred years into the future. Miss Brown didn't half get narked.

MORE THINGS ABOUT ME

Things I like

My lucky number is 7. So why didn't I get fostered by some fantastic rich family when I was seven then?

My favourite colour is blood red, so watch out, ha-ha.

My best friend is Well, I've had heaps and heaps, but Louise has gone off with Justine and now I haven't got anyone just at the moment.

I like eating everything. I like birthday cake best. And any other kind of cake. And smarties and Mars Bars and big buckets of popcorn and jelly spiders and Cornettos and Big Macs with french fries and strawberry milk shakes.

My favourite name is Camilla. There was a lovely little baby at this other home and that was her name. She was a really sweet kid with fantastic hair that I used to try to get into loads of little plaits and I must have hurt her sometimes but she never cried.

She really liked me, little Camilla. She got fostered quick as a wink. I begged her foster mum and dad to bring her back to see me but they never did. ⭐

What did you learn about Tracy from this page?

I like drinking   pints of bitter. That's a joke. I have had a sip of lager once but I didn't like it.

My favourite game is   playing with make-up. Louise and I once borrowed some from Adele who's got heaps. Louise was a bit boring and just tried to make herself look beautiful.

I turned myself into an incredible vampire with evil shadowy eyes and blood dribbling down my chin. I didn't half scare the little ones.

My favourite animal is   Well, there's a rabbit called Lettuce at this home but it's a bit limp, like its name. It doesn't sit up and give you a friendly lick like a dog. I think I'd like a Rottweiler — and then all my enemies had better WATCH OUT.

My favourite TV programme is   horror films.

Best of all I like being with my mum.

Things I don't like
The name   Justine, Louise. Peter. Oh there's heaps and heaps of names I can't stand.

Eating   stew. Especially when it's got great fatty lumps in it. I used to have this horrid foster mother called Aunty Peggy and she was an awful cook. She used to make this slimy stew like molten sick and we were supposed to eat it all up, every single bit. Yuck.

Most of all I hate   Justine. That Monster Gorilla. And not seeing my mum. ⭐

⭐ Tracy has lots of attitude. Find examples.

1. What colour is Tracy's hair?
2. Why did Miss Brown get annoyed with Tracy?
3. What are Tracy's favourite foods?

4. Of all the people Tracy mentions in the story, there are only two that she really likes. Find the names of these two people.
5. Do you think Tracy is happy? Find some examples to back up your answer.
6. Find some examples of humour in the chapter.

7. Does Tracy believe in making wishes? Why do you think this? If you were Tracy, what would you wish?
8. Where does Tracy live, do you think?
9. Tracy mentions one person who really liked her. Who was this? How does this make Tracy feel?
10. How do you think Tracy feels about her Mum? Why do you think this?
11. Would you like to be friends with Tracy? Why?

12. Make a fact file about yourself. Illustrate it.

The Lion, the Witch and the Wardrobe

C.S. Lewis

Lucy was on holiday with her sister and two brothers. They were staying in a big old house that had lots of rooms. One wet day, while they were exploring, they came across a room with a large wardrobe in it. The others thought there was nothing of interest there and left the room. Lucy, however, wanted to see what was in the wardrobe. What a shock she got when the back of the wardrobe opened into a magical country, covered in snow. After walking for a while, she came to a lamp-post and there she met a strange creature, a faun.

Chapter two: What Lucy found there

'Good evening', said Lucy. But the Faun was so busy picking up its parcels that at first it did not reply. When it had finished it made her a little bow.
'Good evening, good evening', said the Faun. 'Excuse me – I don't want to be inquisitive – but should I be right in thinking that you are a Daughter of Eve?'
'My name's Lucy', said she, not quite understanding him.
'But you are – forgive me – you are what they call a girl?' said the Faun.
'Of course I'm a girl', said Lucy.
'You are in fact Human?'
'Of course I'm human', said Lucy, still a little puzzled.
'To be sure, to be sure', said the Faun. 'How stupid of me! But I've never seen a Son of Adam or a Daughter of Eve before. I am delighted. That is to say – 'and then it stopped as if it had been going to say something it had not intended but had remembered in time. 'Delighted, delighted', it went on. 'Allow me to introduce myself. My name is Tumnus.'
'I am very pleased to meet you, Mr Tumnus', said Lucy.
'And may I ask, O Lucy Daughter of Eve', said Mr Tumnus, 'how you have come into Narnia?'

'Narnia? What's that?' said Lucy.

'This is the land of Narnia,' said the Faun, 'where we are now; all that lies between the lamp-post and the great castle of Cair Paravel on the eastern sea. And you – you have come from the wild woods of the west?'

'I – I got in through the wardrobe in the spare room,' said Lucy.

'Ah!' said Mr Tumnus in a rather melancholy voice, 'if only I had worked harder at geography when I was a little Faun, I should no doubt know all about those strange countries. It is too late now.'

'But they aren't countries at all,' said Lucy, almost laughing. 'It's only just back there – at least – I'm not sure. It is summer there.'

'Meanwhile,' said Mr Tumnus, 'it is winter in Narnia, and has been for ever so long, and we shall both catch cold if we stand here talking in the snow. Daughter of Eve from the far land of Spare Oom where eternal summer reigns around the bright city of War Drobe, how would it be if you came and had tea with me?'

'Thank you very much, Mr Tumnus,' said Lucy. 'But I was wondering whether I ought to be getting back.'

'It's only just round the corner,' said the Faun, 'and there'll be a roaring fire – and toast – and sardines – and cake.'

'Well, it's very kind of you,' said Lucy. 'But I shan't be able to stay long.'

'If you will take my arm, Daughter of Eve,' said Mr Tumnus, 'I shall be able to hold the umbrella over both of us. That's the way. Now – off we go.' ☆

☆ How does the writer build up suspense so far?

And so Lucy found herself walking through the wood arm in arm with this strange creature as if they had known one another all their lives.

They had not gone far before they came to a place where the ground became rough and there were rocks all about and little hills up and little hills down. At the bottom of one small valley Mr Tumnus turned suddenly aside as if he were going to walk straight into an unusually large rock, but at the last moment Lucy found he was leading her into the entrance of a cave. As soon as they were inside she found herself blinking in the light of a wood fire. Then Mr Tumnus stooped and took a flaming piece of wood out of the fire with a neat little pair of tongs, and lit a lamp. 'Now we shan't be long,' he said, and immediately put a kettle on. Lucy thought she had never been in a nicer place. It was a little, dry, clean cave of reddish stone with a carpet on the floor and two little chairs ('one for me and one for a friend,' said Mr Tumnus) and a table and a dresser and a mantelpiece over the fire and above that a picture of an old Faun with a grey beard. In one corner there was a door which Lucy thought must lead to Mr Tumnus's bedroom, and on one wall was a shelf full of books. Lucy looked at these while he was setting out the tea things. They had titles like *The Life and Letters of Silenus* or *Nymphs and Their Ways* or *Men, Monks and Gamekeepers; a Study in Popular Legend* or *Is Man a Myth?*' ⭐

'Now, Daughter of Eve!' said the Faun.

And really it was a wonderful tea. There was a nice brown egg, lightly boiled, for each of them, and then sardines on toast, and then buttered toast, and then toast with honey, and then a sugar-topped cake. And when Lucy was tired of eating the Faun began to talk. He had wonderful tales to tell of life in the forest.

He told about the midnight dances and how the Nymphs who lived in the wells and the Dryads who lived in the trees came out to dance with the Fauns; about long, hunting parties after the milk-white stag who could give you wishes if you caught him; about feasting and treasure-seeking with the wild Red Dwarfs in deep mines and caverns far beneath the forest floor; and then about summer when the woods were green and old Silenus on his fat donkey would come to visit them, and sometimes Bacchus himself, and then the streams would run with wine instead of water and the whole forest would give itself up to jollification for weeks on end.

'Not that it isn't always winter now,' he added gloomily. Then to cheer himself up he took out from its case on the dresser a strange little flute that looked as if it were made of straw and began to play. And the tune he played made Lucy want to cry and laugh and dance and go to sleep all at the same time. It must have been hours later when she

⭐ What does the faun's home tell us about him?

shook herself and said:

'Oh, Mr Tumnus – I'm so sorry to stop you, and I do love that tune – but really, I must go home. I only meant to stay for a few minutes.'

'It's no good *now* you know,' said the Faun, laying down its flute and shaking its head at her very sorrowfully.

'No good?' said Lucy, jumping up and feeling rather frightened. 'What do you mean? I've got to go home at once. The others will be wondering what has happened to me.' But a moment later she asked, 'Mr Tumnus! Whatever is the matter?' for the Faun's brown eyes had filled with tears and then the tears began trickling down its cheeks, and soon they were running off the end of its nose; and at last it covered its face with its hands and began to howl.

'Mr Tumnus! Mr Tumnus!' said Lucy in great distress. 'Don't! Don't! What is the matter? Aren't you well? Dear Mr Tumus, do tell me what is wrong.' But the Faun continued sobbing as if its heart would break. And even when Lucy went over and put her arms around him and lent him her handkerchief, he did not stop. He merely took the handkerchief and kept on using it, wringing it out with both hands whenever it got too wet to be any more use, so that presently Lucy was standing in a damp patch.

'Mr Tumnus!' bawled Lucy in his ear, shaking him. 'Do stop. Stop it at once! You ought to be ashamed of yourself, a great bit Faun like you. What on earth are you crying about?'

'Oh – oh – oh!' sobbed Mr Tumnus, 'I'm crying because I'm such a bad Faun.' ⭐

⭐ The mood changes on this page. What do you think is wrong?

101

'I don't think you're a bad Faun at all,' said Lucy.

'I think you are a very good Faun. You are the nicest Faun I've ever met.'

'Oh – oh – you wouldn't say that if you knew,' replied Mr Tumnus between his sobs. 'No, I'm a bad Faun. I don't suppose there ever was a worse Faun since the beginning of the world.'

'But what have you done?' asked Lucy.

'My old father, now,' said Mr Tumnus; 'that's his picture over the mantelpiece. He would never have done a thing like this.'

'A thing like what?' said Lucy.

'Like what I've done,' said the Faun. 'Taken service under the White Witch. That's what I am. I'm in the pay of the White Witch.'

'The White Witch? Who is she?'

'Why, it is she that has got all Narnia under her thumb. It's she that makes it always winter. Always winter and never Christmas; think of that!'

'How awful!' said Lucy. 'But what does she pay *you* for?'

'That's the worst of it,' said Mr Tumnus with a deep groan. 'I'm a kidnapper for her, that's what I am. Look at me, Daughter of Eve. Would you believe that I'm the sort of Faun to meet a poor innocent child in the wood, one that had never done me any harm, and pretend to be friendly with it, and invite it home to my cave, all for the sake of lulling it asleep and then handing it over to the White Witch?'

'No,' said Lucy. 'I'm sure you wouldn't do anything of the sort.'

'But I have,' said the Faun.

'Well,' said Lucy rather slowly (for she wanted to be truthful and yet not be too hard on him), 'well that was pretty bad. But you're so sorry for it that I'm sure you will never do it again.'

'Daughter of Eve, don't you understand?' said the Faun. 'It isn't something I *have* done. I'm doing it now, this very moment.'

'What do you mean?' cried Lucy, turning very white.

'You are the child,' said Tumnus. 'I had orders from the White Witch that if ever I saw a Son of Adam or a Daughter of Eve in the wood, I was to catch them and hand them over to her. And you are the first I ever met. And I've pretended to be your friend and asked you to tea, and all the time I've been meaning to wait till you were asleep and then go and tell *Her.*'

'Oh, but you won't, Mr Tumnus,' said Lucy. 'You won't, will you? Indeed, indeed

Why do you think Lucy turned white?

you really mustn't.'

'And if I don't,' said he, beginning to cry again, 'she's sure to find out. And she'll have my tail cut off, and my horns sawn off, and my beard plucked out, and she'll wave her wand over my beautiful cloven hoofs and turn them into horrid solid hoofs like a wretched horse's. And if she is extra and specially angry she'll turn me into stone and I shall be only a statue of a Faun in her horrible house until the four thrones at Cair Paravel are filled – and goodness knows when that will happen, or whether it will ever happen at all.'

'I'm very sorry, Mr Tumnus,' said Lucy. 'But please let me go home.'

'Of course I will,' said the Faun. 'Of course I've got to. I see that now. I hadn't known what Humans were like before I met you. Of course I can't give you up to the Witch; not now that I know you. But we must be off at once. I'll see you back to the lamp-post. I suppose you can find your own way from there back to Spare Oom and War Drobe?'

'I'm sure I can,' said Lucy.

'We must go as quietly as we can,' said Mr Tumnus. 'The whole wood is full of *her* spies. Even some of the trees are on her side.'

They both got up and left the tea things on the table, and Mr Tumnus once more put up his umbrella and gave Lucy his arm, and they went out into the snow. The journey back was not at all like the journey to the Faun's cave; they stole along as quickly as they could, without speaking a word, and Mr Tumnus kept to the darkest places. Lucy was relieved when they reached the lamp-post again.

'Do you know your way from here, Daughter of Eve?' said Tumnus.

Lucy looked very hard between the trees and could just see in the distance a patch of light that looked like daylight. 'Yes,' she said, 'I can see the wardrobe door.'

'Then be off home as quick as you can,' said the Faun, 'and – c-can you ever forgive me for what I meant to do?'

'Why, of course I can,' said Lucy, shaking him heartily by the hand. 'And I do hope you won't get into dreadful trouble on my account.'

'Farewell, Daughter of Eve,' said he. 'Perhaps I may keep the handkerchief?'

'Rather!' said Lucy, and then ran towards the far off patch of daylight as quickly as her legs would carry her. And presently instead of rough branches brushing past her she felt coats, and instead of crunching snow under her feet she felt wooden boards, and all at once she found herself jumping out of the wardrobe into the same empty room from which the whole adventure had started. She shut the wardrobe door tightly behind her and looked around, panting for breath. It was still raining and she could hear the voices of the others in the passage.

'I'm here,' she shouted. 'I'm here. I've come back, I'm all right.'

1. What was the name of the country that Lucy had entered?
2. What bad thing had the Faun done?

3. Describe the food that Lucy ate.
4. Narnia is a fantasy world. What elements of fantasy can you find in the extract?
5. The White Witch is a wicked character. How does the writer build up this picture of her?

6. How do you know that the Faun lived alone?
7. Why, do you think, did the Faun spend so long telling stories and playing music?
8. Why did the Faun change his mind about handing Lucy over to the White Witch?
9. Why, do you think, does the White Witch want to kidnap a child?
10. What do you think Lucy will tell her sister and brothers?
11. Do you think she will return to Narnia? If you were Lucy would you return?

12. Have you read books or seen films about people entering magical worlds? Talk about it.

The Witches
Roald Dahl

'Down with children! Do them in!
Boil their bones and fry their skin!
Bish them, sqvish them, bash
them, mash them!
Brrreak them, shake them, slash
them, smash them!
Offer chocs vith magic powder!
Say "Eat up!" then say it louder.
Crrram them full of sticky eats,
Send them home still guzzling sveets.
And in the morning little fools
Go marching off to separate schools.
A girl feels sick and goes all pale.
She yells, "Hey look! I've
grrrown a tail!"
A boy who's standing next to her
Screams, "Help! I think I'm
grrrowing fur!"
Another shouts, "Vee look like frrreaks!
There's viskers growing on our cheeks!"
A boy who vos extremely tall
Cries out, "Vot's wrong? I'm grrrowing small!"
Four tiny legs begin to sprrrout
From everybody rrround about.
And all at vunce, all in a trrrice,
There are no children! Only MICE!

In every school is mice galore
All rrrunning rrrround the school-rrroom floor!
And all the poor demented teachers
Is yelling, "Hey, who are these crrreatures?"
They stand upon the desks and shout,
"Get out, you filthy mice! Get out!
Vill someone fetch some mouse-trrraps, please!
And don't forrrget to bring the cheese!"
Now mousetrrraps come and every trrrap
Goes *snippy-snip* and *snappy-snap*.
The mouse-trrraps have a powerful spring,
The springs go *crack* and *snap* and *ping*!
Is lovely noise for us to hear!
Is music to a vitch's ear!
Dead mice is every place arrround,
Piled two feet deep upon the grrround,
Vith teachers searching left and rrright,
But not a single child in sight!
The teachers cry, "Vot's going on?
Oh vhere have all the children gone?
Is half-past nine and as a rrrule
They're never late as this for school!"
Poor teachers don't know vot to do.
Some sit and rrread, and just a few
Amuse themselves throughout the day
By sweeping all the mice avay.
AND ALL US VITCHES SHOUT HOORAY!'

1. Read the title. Look at the pictures. Make a prediction about the story.
2. Have you read other stories or seen films or programmes about space?
3. Do you think that there is life on other planets? Talk about it.

This is not Earth

Tony Bradman

Jamie was skimming along a dried-up river bed on his hover-bike when his helmet radio buzzed for the third time. He tried to ignore it and concentrate on the sheer joy of the ride, the cool wind in his face, the planet's pink sky above, the purple sand sweeping past beneath him. But the buzzing wouldn't go away. It kept on and on, like the irritating whine of an insect trapped inside his ear. Eventually, Jamie could stand it no more, and

slowed the hover-bike to a stop. He had known all along that he couldn't avoid speaking to his parents.

'Hey, Dad,' he said. He didn't have to touch anything on the helmet – the reply function was voice activated. 'Er ... what can I do for you?'

'Well, you could answer your radio for a start,' said his father. 'This is the third time we've tried to call you. We were beginning to get worried.' ☆

'Sorry,' said Jamie. 'I should have realised you'd want to stop me having *fun*. It's probably bad for me to be out *in the open air*.'

☆ Why do you think Jamie's Dad rang him?

108

Jamie had always been close to his mum and dad, and wouldn't usually have talked to them like that, but a few weeks ago he had guessed what they were planning, and he'd been angry with them ever since. So there had been a lot of arguments. Today, however, it seemed that Dad had no intention of reacting to his son's tone of voice.

'Just come home, Jamie,' he said with a sigh. 'We need to talk.'

'I can't *wait*,' muttered Jamie, and angrily broke the connection. He boosted the power on the hover-bike once more, rose out of the river bed, and grimly headed back towards his parents' farm.

The surface of the planet stretched before him – a dusty, purple plain ringed by hills, with colossal, white-capped mountains rising beyond. It was an alien world, slightly smaller than Earth and orbiting a distant star, a red giant. But Jamie didn't think of it as alien, for he had never lived in humanity's original home. Of course he had seen films of Earth, and pictures of the beautiful place it had been before endless wars and pollution finally ruined it for human life.

The survivors had abandoned the wrecked cities and dying lands and poisoned oceans, and taken off in a fleet of starships to find somewhere else to live. Jamie's parents had met on the *Galileo* in the first few months after The Great Exodus, as it was now called. And that's where Jamie had been born, 12 Earth-years ago – in deep space.

Until a while back, all he had known was life on a starship. If you could call it life. Jamie scowled as he remembered the *Galileo*. Dozens of families packed into a filthy tin can, the air stale, the food produced by machines and almost inedible, disputes always breaking out because nobody had any privacy. Then there was the sickness the doctors couldn't cure, however hard they tried. Space Fever killed many, and left the lucky ones – like Jamie – with nasty sores to remember it by. The sores were often raw and painful, and seemed permanent. Jamie and his parents had hoped that living on a planet might help, but it hadn't. ✦

Jamie reached the crest of a hill and let the hover-bike slow to a stop again. He sat there for a moment looking down on the farm, a cluster of silver domes in a small valley. He scratched the weeping sore on his hand and thought of the day when he and his parents had landed. He'd been happy enough when he'd found out they'd been given the chance to colonise a planet, even one that didn't have a name, only a code number, K1754. But he'd never imagined just how incredible it would be.

> ✦ Why did Jamie's family think that living on a planet might help?

The clean, crisp freshness of the air, the sense of wide-open spaces and total freedom – Jamie loved the place from the moment he stepped out of the shuttle craft that had brought them down from the starship.

In the year since then, Jamie had spent as much time as he could roaming on the hover-bike his dad had built for him. The planet was mostly desert, with scant rainfall and few plants. There weren't many animals either, apart from a squirrel-like rodent, some tiny reptiles, and strange flying creatures that resembled large bats. Even so, the more Jamie got to know this world, the more it felt like the home he had always wanted. But his parents didn't feel the same, and that was the problem. ⭐

Jamie's helmet radio buzzed once more. 'OK, OK,' he sighed, zooming off down the hill. 'I'm, on my way ...'

As he skimmed along, Jamie tried not to look at the fields his parents had planted using frozen seeds from the *Galileo's* gene banks – the wheat struggling to survive, the stunted vegetables, the dead fruit-tree saplings. Jamie stopped by the entrance to the largest dome, the family's living quarters. He got off his hover-bike and removed his helmet, took a deep breath, touched the panel that opened the door ... and went inside.

As usual, his parents were busy. Dad was in the kitchen area preparing the evening meal, Mum was working on the computer probably checking their stores. There wasn't much space inside, but it was like a palace compared to the tiny cabin they'd had back on the *Galileo*. The dome was divided into three, the kitchen/living room and two sleeping areas, so Jamie even had his own bedroom.

'Dinner will be in ten minutes,' said Dad, glancing at him and smiling nervously. 'It's your favourite ... chicken stew with vegetables.'

Jamie shrugged. Dad's stew wasn't bad, but it wasn't that great, either. The chicken wasn't real, of course, but some kind of substitute made on the *Galileo*. They'd brought a lot of food with them, which was just as well. But they were still a long way from being self-sufficient.

'And then after dinner we're going to watch a movie,' said Mum, smiling too. 'It's time we did something nice together as a family.'

'What, instead of arguing?' muttered Jamie. 'I thought Dad said we needed to talk. I know what you're going to say anyway, so let's get it over with.'

'Don't be like that, Jamie,' said Mum. She came over to put an arm around him, but he pulled away. 'We're only thinking of you ...'

'Oh, yeah?' said Jamie. 'That's not how it feels to me. I want to stay here, but you

⭐ Why do you think Jamie's parents didn't feel the same?

don't. We're going back to the *Galileo*, aren't we?'

Jamie's parents looked at each other, their smiles gone now.

'We don't really have much choice,' Dad said quietly, his shoulders sagging as if he were very, very tired. 'You know how hard your mum and I have tried, but we just can't make the farm work. None of the crops we've planted are thriving.'

'Maybe they need more time,' said Jamie.

'You're not giving them a proper chance. They're Earth plants and, if you haven't noticed, this is not Earth. They might do OK in a couple of years ...'

'You may be right,' said Mum. 'But I'm afraid we don't have time to wait. The truth is we're going to run out of food in a couple of *weeks*, and the captain of the *Galileo* won't give us supplies after that. Not unless we can give him something in return.'

'And that's not likely to happen, is it?' said Dad. He started ladling the stew into bowls, then paused to smile at his son again. 'Come on Jamie, don't be cross. We'll only be on the *Galileo* a while, until they find another planet for us. A few months won't be so bad, will it?'

'But I like *this* planet,' Jamie yelled. 'I don't want to try anywhere else. And what if they don't find one we can settle on? You told me there aren't many planets with an atmosphere people can breathe, or where it's not too hot or too cold. We might be stuck on the *Galileo* forever!' ⭐

'We don't want that any more than you do,' said Mum. 'We'd love to stay here. We'd give anything to make it possible. But we can't. So that's it, end of story. I'm sorry, Jamie. The shuttle is coming to collect us ... tomorrow.' ⭐

Jamie felt as if all the blood had suddenly drained out of his body. His parents were looking at him, obviously waiting for him to speak, to argue with them. He opened his mouth to do just that, but what could he say that hadn't already been said? So he closed it, then turned on his heel and went into his bedroom, slamming the flimsy plastic door behind him.

Jamie stayed in his room all evening, refusing to come out and watch the movie or speak to his parents. Dad brought him a bowl of stew, which he left untouched, and Mum tried to talk to him. But Jamie was playing a computer game and wouldn't look at her. He was more angry than ever, and he wanted them to know it. ⭐

When they put their heads round the door to say goodnight, Jamie ignored them,

⭐ Do you think Jamie was being reasonable or not? Why do you think this?

⭐ Do you think Jamie will accept his parents' decision?

⭐ What words on this page show the tension between Jamie and his parents?

although he did get into bed. Then he lay there, unable to sleep, scratching at his sores and remembering all the things he hated about the *Galileo* – the overcrowding, the people suffering from Space Fever ... He felt sick just thinking that the next time he went to bed it would be in a cramped little cabin with Mum and Dad squeezed in beside him.

Suddenly Jamie knew he would much rather stay on the planet and die than get on the shuttle tomorrow and fly back into space. So why didn't he do just that? He could simply run away and hide. He knew the place much better than Mum and Dad – they would never find him. A few last days of freedom would be worth more than a whole life-time on board the *Galileo*. He sat up and quickly started to put on his clothes. Not that he really wanted to die, of course ... ⭐

Jamie carefully slipped from his bedroom and crept over to the kitchen area. He put a handful of energy snacks in his backpack, added a big bottle of water from the fridge, then made for the main door. He was pretty sure Mum and Dad wouldn't hear him. Dad said they were usually so tired they slept like the dead. Even so, Jamie's heart was hammering hard as he touched the panel and the door hissed open.

⭐ **What thoughts do you think are going through Jamie's mind now?**

Outside, the planet's three small moons were shining, so there was plenty of light to see by. Jamie pulled on his helmet and climbed on to the hover-bike. Soon he was heading away from the farm, back up into the hills, grateful that the hover-bike's motor was almost silent. With a bit of luck, Mum and Dad wouldn't discover he was gone until the morning.

Jamie skimmed along, an eerie, triple shadow gliding over the dark sand beside him. The wind was colder than it had been earlier, and he knew the temperature would drop even further during the night. He was wearing his thick, outdoors jacket, so he should be OK. But it would still be good to spend a few hours under shelter if he could, and maybe get some sleep. He knew just the right place, too – a valley with a small pond and a cave on the slope nearby.

By the time he reached the mouth of the cave, two of the moons had gone down, and most of the valley was in darkness. The place was the same as ever, although Jamie noticed there were some new, tall plants around the pond. He couldn't see them clearly, but was too tired to look at them closely right now. Moments later, after checking the cave was empty, Jamie settled in for the night. ⭐

He slept on the sand just inside the cave, wrapped in his jacket, head on his backpack. It was a restless, dream-filled sleep, and he was glad to be woken by the warm rays of the sun touching his face. Jamie stood and stretched, his body stiff and aching. He opened his backpack, took out an energy snack and drank some water. He wondered if Mum and Dad had discovered that he'd run away.

As if on cue, his helmet radio started buzzing. It was sitting on the seat of his hover-bike, where he'd left it last night. Jamie went over to pick it up, tempted to answer. He was beginning to feel he'd done something stupid, and that it was wrong to worry Mum and Dad.

Then he saw the plants by the pond in the clear light of day. There was something rather strange about them, so ignoring the buzzing noise, he went down the slope for a closer look.

The plants had thick, tall stems, and were clustered along one edge of the pond, where they could get most sunlight. But it was their leaves that had caught Jamie's attention. They were dark red and grew directly out of the stems in pairs, one on either side, perhaps 20 pairs to a plant. Jamie reached out to touch a leaf and, as he did so, the tip of another one brushed against the sore on his hand. The skin around it instantly began to tingle, and he snatched it back. Then the tingling became more intense...

⭐ What do you think Jamie was checking the cave for?

113

Jamie watched in amazement as the sore on his hand vanished. He rubbed at the skin, but where it had once been raw and painful, it was now healed. Jamie broke off a different leaf from a second plant and cautiously rubbed it over a sore on his arm. Exactly the same thing happened. It was incredible – and then Jamie realised how important this discovery could be. The planet itself, good old K1754, might just have given him the solution to his problem. Maybe this was a cure for Space Fever ...

He ran back up the slope, picked up his helmet, and quickly put it on. 'Jamie calling Mum and Dad', he gabbled. 'Can you hear me?'

'Jamie!' said his dad. 'Where are you? We've been so worried.'

'Listen, Dad', said Jamie. 'You said we'd only be able to stay here if we had something we could give the captain of the *Galileo* in return for more supplies. Well, you're not going to believe what I've found ...

'What are you talking about?' said Dad. 'Are you sure you're OK?'

'Relax, Dad, I'm fine', said Jamie. He looked down at the red leaf in his hand. 'In fact, I've never felt better. I'll see you and Mum in a while.' ☆

☆ Jamie's tone changes at this point in the story. Find words that show this.

Moments later, Jamie was skimming along on his hover-bike once more, the cool wind in his face, the pink sky above and purple sand beneath him. His pockets were stuffed with red leaves, and he was smiling. And this time it felt good to be going home.

1. Why did Jamie's family have to leave Earth?
2. Why did Jamie not like living on the spaceship *Galileo*?
3. Describe the family's new living quarters.

4. This story is set in space. Scan the text and find as many words as you can that tell this.
5. Jamie's parents try hard not to quarrel with him. Find examples of this throughout the story.
6. Jamie's tone towards his parents is sarcastic at times. Find some sentences that show this.
7. There are a number of clues that the planet is not thriving. How many can you find?

8. How far into the future do you think this story is set? Why do you think this?
9. How do you think Jamie's discovery will change life on the planet for his family?
10. What might have happened next in the story if Jamie had not discovered the plants?

11. How do you think you would react if your family was cut off from society?
12. Jamie's parents had to leave Earth because of wars and pollution there. Talk about any books you have read or films you have seen about people having to leave their homes because of some disaster/tragedy.

People in space

1. Read the headings in this unit. What kind of information do you expect to find under each one?

Have you ever thought about becoming an astronaut? First you have to study Science, both in school and university. Then you have to be specially trained. Russia and the United States are the two main countries where you can train to become an astronaut. Russian astronauts are called cosmonauts.

Special training

When a rocket takes off, there is a huge force on the astronauts' bodies. To cope with this force, astronauts need to be very fit and strong.

Life in space can be very tricky. Without the pull of gravity everyone and everything is weightless and floats about. Before astronauts go into orbit, they have special training to

Astronauts floating in the 'vomit comet'.

prepare them for the feeling of weightlessness in space. This training takes place inside a special aeroplane, nicknamed the 'Vomit Comet'. The astronauts float around inside this special plane as if they were in orbit.

Astronauts need to get used to spinning and turning at different angles when they are floating in space. In training, they strap themselves to spinning machines to prepare for this.

Astronauts also rehearse for space walks and missions under water. A special swimming pool is filled with very salty water, which makes the astronauts float as if they were in space.

Types of astronauts

There are two types of astronaut: mission specialists and space pilots. Mission specialists are engineers or scientists who train to become astronauts. They carry out science experiments and satellite repairs in space.

Space pilots fly spacecraft. Spacecraft are much faster and more complicated than the fastest aeroplanes, so new space pilots must already be jet pilots.

Life in space

Eating and drinking in space is very difficult because everything floats. Astronauts have to suck food out of tubes so that the food doesn't get into their equipment. If astronauts want salt or pepper in their food, water has to be added to it first or it would float away and possibly damage instruments or get into their eyes. Knives and forks are magnetised so that they will cling to the tray and not drift around.

Astronauts sleep in sleeping bags strapped to the wall. Otherwise they would spend the night floating around. At night they wear earplugs to block out the noise of the air conditioning and the machines in the spacecraft.

While in the spacecraft, astronauts wear normal everyday clothing but if they have to leave the spacecraft, they must wear their spacesuits to protect them from radiation and other dangers in space.

Space stations

A space station is a large spacecraft that stays in orbit around Earth. Scientists can live and work there for long periods of time. The first space station launched was the American Skylab in 1976. Although early space stations could be launched

on one rocket, they are now so big that they have to be sent into space piece by piece. The newest space station is the International Space Station (ISS).This project is the result of many countries coming together and co-operating with one another, including the USA, Russia, Japan and some European countries. The first part of it was launched in 1998 and it was still not completed in 2011. When finished it will be the size of a football pitch and weigh as much as 450 small cars. The ISS is the biggest man-made satellite to orbit Earth and can be seen with the naked eye at night. It travels so fast that it orbits Earth 17 times a day! Solar panels on the space station provide power. The station contains two bathrooms and a gymnasium. Up to seven astronauts can live and work together in the space station.

Astronauts can become very ill if they stay in space too long. Lack of exercise and weightlessness can damage bones and muscles. Astronauts may also be affected by the harmful rays of the sun because they don't have the earth's atmosphere to protect them.

Space timeline

	Mission	Purpose
1957	Sputnik	First satellite in orbit
1957	Sputnik 2	First animal in orbit (a dog called Laika)
1961	Vostok 1	First man in orbit (Yuri Gagarin)
1963	Vostok 6	First woman in orbit (Valentina Tereshkova)
1969	Apollo 11	First landing on the Moon
1973	Skylab	First space station
1981	Columbia	First space shuttle
1986	MIR	Space station built from modules
1993	Mars Observer	Space probe sent to orbit Mars
1997	Pathfinder	Robot space craft lands on Mars
2001		First astronauts to live on the International Space Station
2001		American millionaire Denis Tito pays about 20 million dollars to become the world's first space tourist
2011		US government ends the space shuttle programme

Did you know?

The person to spend the longest time in space was a Russian cosmonaut who stayed on the space station MIR for 435 days, beginning in 1994.

Astronauts grow taller in space! Due to the lack of gravity the spine expands and the astronaut grows by between five and six centimetres!

Yuri Gagarin

The first man to travel into space was Yuri Gagarin from Russia. He had trained as a fighter pilot. On April 12, 1961 he orbited Earth in his spaceship Vostok 1. This was Gagarin's only space mission. He died eight years later in a plane crash.

The word astronaut means 'sailor of the stars'. The Russian word cosmonaut means 'sailor of the universe'.

Valentina Tereshkova

The first woman to travel in space was Valentina Tereshkova, also from Russia. Her father was a tractor driver and her mother worked in a clothing factory. In March 1963 she spent over 70 hours in space and her spaceship orbited Earth 48 times!

1. Name the two countries that train the most astronauts.
2. List the different ways in which astronauts prepare for space.
3. Choose one of the milestones from the space timeline and find out as much as you can about it.
4. What extra milestones might be on the timeline for the year 3012?

My Rocket Dreamed ...

Paul Cookson

My rocket dreamed of circling the
    earth,
orbiting the moon,
zigzagging planets,
Looping the loop with satellites,
dodging meteorites,
racing comets
and disappearing into time warps
    and black holes.

Instead, it circled the garden shed,
orbited the swing,
zigzagged the apple tree,
looped the loop with the clothes line,
dodged two butterflies,
raced one wasp and a bluebottle
then disappeared over the hedge
into the time warp and black hole
that is Mr Hislop's back garden.

Stone Fox

John Reynolds Gardiner

Little Willy has a big job to do. His Grandfather refuses to get out of bed, so it is up to Willy alone to save their farm from the tax collector. But where can a ten-year-old get five hundred dollars in a hurry? Then Willy sees the poster for the National Dogsled Race.

Little Willy went to see Mayor Smiley at the city hall building in town to sign up for the race. The mayor's office was large and smelled like hair tonic.

The mayor sat in a bright red chair with his feet on his desk. There was nothing on the desk except the mayor's feet.

'We have a race for you youngsters one hour before.' Mayor Smiley mopped sweat from his neck with a silk handkerchief, although little Willy thought it was quite cool in the room.

'I wanna enter the *real* race, Mr Mayor.'

'You must be funning, boy.' The mayor laughed twice and blotted his neck.

'Anyway, there's an entrance fee.'

'How much?'

'Fifty dollars.'

Little Willy was stunned. That was a lot of money just to enter a race. But he was determined. He ran across the street to the bank.

'Don't be stupid,' Mr Foster told little Willy.

'This is not a race for amateurs. Some of the best dog teams in the Northwest will be entering.'

'I have Searchlight! We go fast as lightning. Really, Mr Foster, we do.'

Mr Foster shook his head. 'You don't stand a chance of winning.'

'Yes, we do!'

'Willy ... the money in your savings account is for your college education. You know I can't give it to you.'

'You have to.'

'I do?'

'It's *my* money!'

Little Willy left the bank with a stack of ten dollar gold pieces – five of them, to be exact.

He walked into the mayor's office and plopped the coins down on the mayor's desk. 'Me and Searchlight are gonna win that five hundred dollars, Mr Mayor. You'll see. Everybody'll see.'

Mayor Smiley counted the money, wiped his neck, and entered little Willy in the race.

When little Willy stepped out of the city hall building, he felt ten feet tall. He looked up and down the snow-covered street. He was grinning from ear to ear. Searchlight walked over and stood in front of the sled, waiting to be hitched up. But little Willy wasn't ready to go yet. He put his thumbs in his belt loops and let the sun warm his face.

He felt great. In his pocket was a map Mayor Smiley had given him showing the ten miles the race covered. Down Main Street, right on North Road – little Willy could hardly hold back his excitement.

What do you learn about little Willy from the way he talks to Mayor Smiley and Mr Foster?

Five miles of the race he travelled every day and knew with his eyes closed. The last five miles were back into town along South Road, which was mostly straight and flat. It's speed that would count here, and with the lead he knew he could get in the first five miles, little Willy was sure he could win.

As little Willy hitched Searchlight to the sled, something down at the end of the street – some moving objects – caught his eye. They were difficult to see because they were all white. There were five of them. And they were beautiful. In fact, they were the most beautiful Samoyeds little Willy had ever seen.

The dogs held their heads up proudly and strutted in unison. They pulled a large but lightly constructed sled. They also pulled a large – but by no means lightly constructed – man. Way down at the end of the street the man looked normal, but as the sled got closer, the man got bigger and bigger.

The man was an Indian – dressed in furs and leather, with moccasins that came all the way up to his knees. His skin was dark, his hair was dark, and he wore a dark-coloured headband. His eyes sparkled in the sunlight, but the rest of his face was as hard as stone.

The sled came to a stop right next to little Willy. The boy's mouth hung open as he tilted his head way back to look up at the man. Little Willy had never seen a giant before.

'Gosh,' little Willy gasped.

The Indian looked at little Willy. His face was solid granite, but his eyes were alive and cunning.

'Howdy,' little Willy blurted out, and he gave a nervous smile.

But the Indian said nothing. His eyes shifted to Searchlight, who let out a soft moan but did not bark. ⭐

The Giant walked into the city hall building.

Word that Stone Fox had entered the race spread throughout the town of Jackson within the hour, and throughout the state of Wyoming within the day.

Stories and legends about the awesome mountain man followed shortly. Little Willy heard many of them at Lester's General Store.

'Was this time in Denver, he snapped a man's back with two fingers,' said Dusty, the town drunk. But nobody believed him really.

Little Willy learned that no white man had ever heard Stone Fox talk. Stone Fox refused to speak with the white man because of the treatment his people had

⭐ Why do you think Searchlight did not bark?

received. His tribe, the Shoshone, who were peaceful seed gatherers, had been forced to leave Utah and settle on a reservation in Wyoming with another tribe called the Arapaho.

Stone Fox's dream was for his people to return to their homeland. Stone Fox was using the money he won from racing to simply buy the land back. He had already purchased four farms and over two hundred acres.

That Stone Fox was smart, all right.

In the next week little Willy and Searchlight went over the ten mile track every day until they knew every inch of it by heart.

Stone Fox hardly practised at all. In fact, little Willy only saw Stone Fox do the course once, and then he sure wasn't going very fast.

The race was scheduled for Saturday morning at ten o'clock. Only nine sleds were entered. Mayor Smiley had hoped for more contestants, but after Stone Fox had entered, well ... you couldn't blame people for wanting to save their money.

It was true Stone Fox had never lost a race. But little Willy wasn't worried. He had made up his mind to win. And nothing was going to stop him. Not even Stone Fox.

⟡ **What do you predict will happen next?**

1. Why did Stone Fox refuse to speak with white people?
2. What was Stone Fox using his winnings for?
3. What preparation did little Willy and Searchlight make before taking part in the race?

4. This story is set in the United States. Find words that show this.
5. How does the author create suspense? Find examples of this.

6. Mr Foster plays a small but important role in the story. Do you agree?
7. Little Willy's mood changes during this story. Find where this happens and say why.
8. Do you think Stone Fox is a good name for the Indian? Why do you think this?
9. Would you like to read what happens next? How does the author keep you interested?

10. What do you know about the history of the Native Americans?
11. Find out about the Native American tribes mentioned in the story.

Clothes around the world

1. Why do you think people in different parts of the world wear different kinds of clothes?
2. From what types of material can clothes be made?

People all over the world wear different clothes made from different materials. Often, what they wear depends on the climate where they live.

Canada

The Inuit of northern Canada have to dress for weather in the Arctic Circle where it is very cold. They wear hooded jackets called *parkas*, trousers and gloves. These used to be made from deerskin or sealskin and decorated with beaded glass or metal.

Andes

People in the Andes make clothes from sheep and llama wool. The women wear brightly coloured woven shawls called *mantas*.

Nigeria

Many women in Nigeria still dress in traditional costume every day. They wear a long loose blouse called a *buba* and a type of wraparound skirt called an *iro*.

India

Many women in India wear *saris*. A sari is a piece of colourful cloth that is wrapped around the body. It can be up to 8 metres long and made from either cotton or silk. A small top called a *choli* is worn under the sari.

Linen

Linen is thought to be the oldest material used by people. It comes from a plant called flax. The Ancient Egyptians used to wrap their dead in linen shrouds.

Cotton

Cotton is the world's most widely-used material. It is made from the long hairs covering the seeds of the cotton-plant. These seeds are called cotton balls.

Wool

Wool has been used to make clothing since ancient times. There are 40 different breeds of sheep. Each of them produces a different sort of wool. Woollen clothing is also made from goat, llama and camel hair.

Silk

Silk is a soft, shimmering material that is made from the cocoon of the silkworm. One cocoon contains about one kilometre of thread. The secret of silk-making was discovered by the Chinese thousands of years ago. This discovery was kept secret for centuries until two monks brought silkworms to India. They hid the silkworms in their walking sticks.

Spain

Many countries have their own traditional costumes which are worn only on special occasions. This photo shows a Spanish dancer in traditional Spanish dress.

Japan

The traditional robes of Japan are called *kimono*, which means 'clothing'. A kimono is a long robe that is tied by a sash called an *obi*. Some obis are four metres long.

Scotland

Every clan in Scotland has its own tartan.
Tartans are woven from coloured woollen
thread. Men in Scotland wear tartan *kilts*. A
kilt is a heavy skirt that fastens at the waist. It
is worn with a type of purse called a *sporran*.
This outfit is now only worn on
special occasions.

China

In China, important people used to wear silk robes.
The robes were embroidered with flowers, birds and
animals. The Emperor of China and his family were
the only people allowed to have dragons on their
robes. The dragon is a Chinese symbol of power,
strength and good luck.

1. Name two kinds of material that we get from:
   a.) plants   b.) animals
2. Where in the world would you find the following clothes:
   a.) obi   b.) manta   c.) buba?
3. Skim through the unit and
   a.) list the countries mentioned
   b.) list all the clothes mentioned. Which are worn every day and which are for
   special occasions?
4. Find another example of everyday clothing from a different part of the world.
5. Can you find other examples of traditional costumes?
6. Find out what kind of clothing was traditionally worn in Ireland.

Dear Norman

ROBERT H. RICHARD

1. Scan through the text. Look at the pictures and text layout. What is unusual about this story?
2. What do you think of the title?

Dear Norman,

Thank you so much for your letter which arrived just before lunch.

It came as quite a surprise when you left with all of your possessions this morning. We did not understand why you left through the back door. Now we know that it was because you have gone to live in your tree house in the back garden.

I am sure that your decision to leave our family is a serious one. Therefore I would like to wish you all the best for the exciting new life you are starting on your own. Please do keep in touch from up there.

Love,
Dad

☆ Why do you think Norman went to live in the tree house?

Dear Norman,

You are very sweet to take the time to write. Thank you for explaining a few of our mistakes in such detail. Your father and I will find your advice very useful as your sister grows up.

I hope that life in your tree house is calming down since you moved in earlier today. I could see from the dining room how difficult it was to carry all your things up that long, steep ladder by yourself. How did you manage to get that big TV set up there? It certainly was clever. Now how will you manage to get electricity for it? I'll bet you have another clever idea!

Did you see those sweet, busy bees swarming around below your tree house porch this afternoon? I suppose they could have been hornets or wasps building a nest, but they looked more like jolly little bumblebees to me.

No doubt you took plenty of food with you up into your tree house. I'm afraid I didn't plan the day as well as you so I have this extra cheese sandwich and a chocolate bar left over. I am sending them up your message rope with this letter in the hope that you can use them in some way.

If you think of any other mistakes your father and I made don't hesitate to get in touch. Meanwhile, lots of love from

Mum

Dear Sir/Madam,

The book you recently ordered: How To Negotiate, has arrived. We will hold the book for you in our shop for 7 days.

Thank you for your order.

The Parkville Book Shop

Dear Norman,
Mum and Dad say, I can have your room. Ha Ha.

Beth

Do you think Norman will change his mind? Why?

130

Dear Norman,

I understand from your parents that I should not expect to see you in school for some time due to changes in your personal life. Please take as much time as you feel you need.

Perhaps school no longer seems important now that you live in a tree house behind your family's home. That makes sense. Geography, Music, History: which of the lessons you missed this morning would be useful in a tree house? None, probably.

What you need are different skills, skills useful for life in the wild: how to keep a small, safe fire burning for light and warmth. How to tell good berries, nuts and mushrooms from deadly ones. Which animals you will compete with for territory. Unfortunately, we don't study any of these at Parkville school. You will have to do most of your learning on your own now, Norman.

If you decide to continue any of your studies with us please send me a note. I cannot send you all of the fun and friendship from our class here at Parkville School, but I can certainly send you the homework!

All best wishes from me and from all your classmates in Room 214.

Mrs Bouquet

Norm,
You don't know me very well but I've seen you around. My message is: go for it. Don't let them push you around. Stay up in that tree house until you get what you want.
Your fan,
Daniel Barleycorn

UNKY
K CHOCOLAT

☆ How do you think Norman is feeling at this point? What do you think he will he do?

Dear Norman,

Thank you for sending me your photograph. You look like a typical Western boy! Here is my photograph. Maybe I look like a typical Japanese girl?

I am glad we are pen pals. Now I can practise my English. Do you want to practise your Japanese? Ha ha.

I am also glad that writing letters is your favourite hobby. What luck for me!

Your Pen Pal,
Mariko

Dear Norman,

I hope you don't mind me putting this message on your rope. I am the guy who has come to fix your family's refrigerator (that's my blue and white van on the drive). Although we have never met I am writing you this note because I moved into my own tree house once when I was a kid. I can't remember the reason.

Anyway, I want you to know that you have my support.

Daryl, Refrigerator Engineer, 38 years old

Hey kid,
Pull yourself together.
You're making a fool of
yourself.
Surrender now.
They'll take you back.
Trust me.
Signed,
Anonymous

☆ Who do you think wrote the anonymous letter? Do you agree with what it says?

132

Dear Norman,

I hope you are well and not spending too much time worrying about your lonely old grandmother. I'm fine most of the time. I do have bad days when none of my grandchildren have visited or telephoned, but I try to remain cheerful.

Your mother says you have been acting strange lately. Stop it; that's not polite.

Next time you speak to my son (your father), please tell him from me (his mother, your grandmother) that it's high time he wrote a letter to his mother (me).

I'm so glad you liked the sweater I sent for your birthday. I had to spend half the day crossing town to get it, and of course it was not cheap. Still, it was worth it if you appreciate it so much.

I can't wait to see all of you next weekend. You are what keeps me happy.

Love,
Grandma

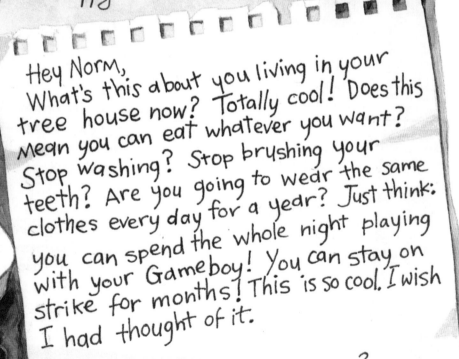

Hey Norm,
What's this about you living in your tree house now? Totally cool! Does this mean you can eat whatever you want? Stop washing? Stop brushing your teeth? Are you going to wear the same clothes every day for a year? Just think: you can spend the whole night playing with your Gameboy! You can stay on strike for months! This is so cool. I wish I had thought of it.

Alfred
P. S. Can I have your bike?

GOOD BOY
MAGAZINES

Dear Occupant,

I am writing to you today with a very special offer.

We at Family Publications would like to send you the next twelve months of _Good Boy_ magazine for only £4.99. What a deal! That's only 42p per issue!

For only 42p you get _Good Boy_ magazine every month. Each issue is packed with ideas to help you become the perfect son and brother:

● How to help your sister do the dishes.
● Cleaning up your room before Mum asks.
● Enjoying garden chores.

Plus there are our regular features: "The Polite Crossword", "Thank You Letter of the Month", and "Table Manners".

Do your entire family a big favour: order today. Don't miss another month's issue of _Good Boy_ magazine!

But wait! That's not all! If you order now we will also send you – absolutely free of charge – a _Good Boy_ baseball cap. Wear it and all your friends will know what a Good Boy you are!

Why not be a Good Boy today?

Order now.

Yours sincerely,
The Marketing Department
Good Boy Magazines
Family Publications

> ☆ Do you think Good Boy Magazines really exists? Who might have sent this letter?

134

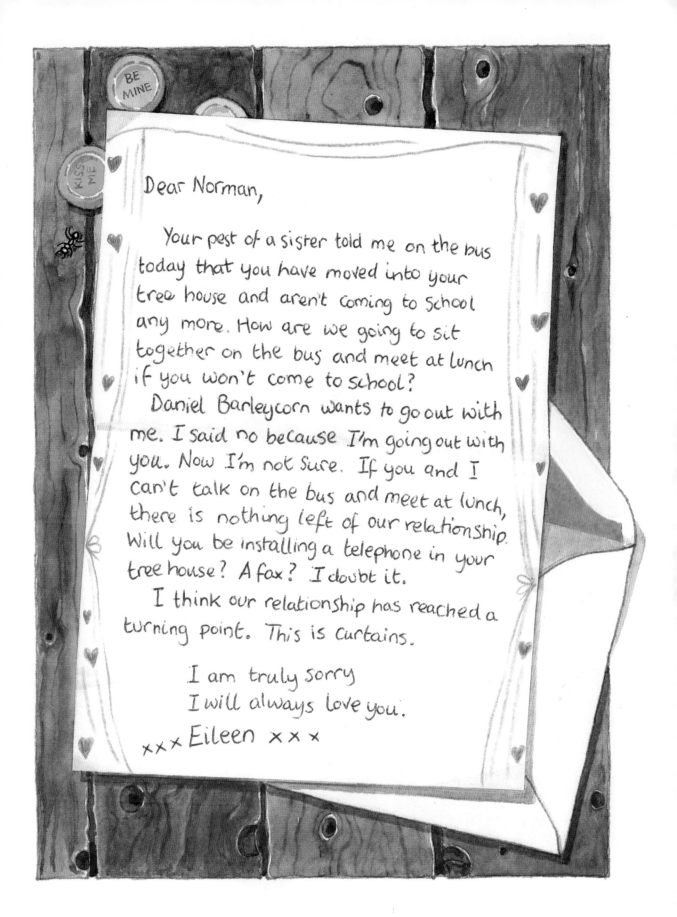

Dear Norman,

You are invited to a Birthday Party

for **Alison Child-**

The most beautiful girl in our school.
Refreshments & Possible Kisses.
Saturday, 11 May, 5 pm.

RSVP

Dear Norman,
 Thank you for your letter explaining why you do not want any pocket money this week. It made your mother and me wonder how much we would save if you continue this practice for the remainder of your childhood.
 10 years × 52 weeks per year × £2 per week pocket money = £1,040 total savings.
(You might want to check our maths.)
 Isn't it amazing the way it adds up?
 Love
 Dad

Dear Norman,

Congratulations! Your essay "Peace Now" has won First Prize in _The Parkville Gazette_'s Solving the World's Problems Contest! The judges were especially impressed by the section "Peace Begins in Your Own Back Garden".

As you know, the First Prize in the Solving the World's Problems Contest is a trip to Washington D.C. where you will visit the White House and actually discuss your essay with the President of the United States. You will be able to take one member of your family with you on this once-in-a-lifetime trip.

Please ask a parent or guardian to contact me as soon as possible to make arrangements for the trip.

And congratulations once again on your wise essay!

Best wishes,
The Editor
The Parkville Gazette

Norman,
Dad said I should write. I miss you. I think you should move back into our house. I don't think you should be on strike any more. It's boring.

I haven't decided yet about letting you have your room back. We can negotiate.

Yours sincerely,
Your sister,
Beth

Dear Norman,
Thank you for your letter. I understand your feelings. It will be okay just to move back into the house. Don't forget to wipe your feet.

Love,
Mum

☆ Why do you think Norman decided to come home?

1. What did Norman take to the tree house with him?
2. How does Norman receive his letters?
3. Why did Eileen break up with Norman?

4. Norman receives a number of letters from his family. How do they differ in their response to him?
5. Which is your favourite letter? Why?

6. Who do you think ordered the book: *How to Negotiate?*
7. 'Thank you for explaining a few of our mistakes in detail.' What do you think Norman had written to his parents?
8. Do you think Noman's parents handled the situation well? Why?
9. How does Norman's family let him know they love him and want him back?
10. How do you think Norman will get on with his parents when he moves back in?
11. If you were writing to Norman what advice would you give him?

12. If you lived in a tree house what challenges would you experience? What would you miss about your home?
13. Name other ways of communicating besides letter writing.

Thank-You Letter

Robin Klein

Dear Aunty Grace, ~~Mum said I had to~~
I'm writing this letter just to say
~~I hate that terrible dress you sent~~
I adore the dress you sent today.

~~Erk! Mauve!~~ The colour's just terrific!
Those little puff sleeves are really neat!
Frilly socks to match! It's just too much!
~~I'd rather wear blisters on my feet!~~

Mum says the dress looks sweetly charming.
It suits me now I'm growing up.
~~When I was made to try that thing on~~
~~I totally felt like throwing up!~~

The lace around the hem's ~~a nightmare –~~
~~I won't wear that ghastly dress!~~ a dream!
I've never seen such pretty ruffles
~~I hope I wake up before I scream!~~

You shouldn't have spent so much money,
But thanks for such a lovely surprise –
~~Of all the dum dum birthday presents,~~
~~Yours, Aunty Grace, easily takes first~~ prize!

You're very generous. ~~With some luck~~
~~I can lose the socks.~~ So thanks again
~~Ink spilled on mauve I hope won't wash out~~
For the wonderful dress! Love from

Jane xx

Dear Mum

Brian Patten

Dear Mum,

while you were out
a cup went and broke itself,
a crack appeared in that old blue vase
your great-great granddad
brought back from Mr Ming in China.
Somehow, without me even turning on the tap,
the sink mysteriously overflowed.
A strange jam stain,
about the size of a boy's hand,
appeared on the kitchen wall.
I don't think we'll ever discover
exactly how the cat
managed to turn on the washing machine,
(specially from the inside),
or how Sis's pet rabbit went and mistook
the waste disposal unit for a burrow.
I can tell you I was scared when,
 as if by magic,
a series of muddy footprints
appeared on the new white carpet.
I was being good
(honest)
but I think the house is haunted so,
knowing you are going to have a fit,
I've gone over to Gran's for a bit.

Guide dogs

1. What do you know about the work of guide dogs?
2. Without a guide dog, how might a blind person get around?
3. What difference does a guide dog make to its owner, do you think?

Guide dogs are trained to help blind or partially-sighted people. They help their owner to get around safely and to lead an independent life. The first school for training guide dogs was set up in Germany. They helped many of the soldiers who returned blind from World War I.

In Ireland

Irish Guide Dogs for the Blind was founded in 1976. It helps people who are blind or partially-sighted. It also helps families of children with autism. Its headquarters and training centre is in Cork. Both the dogs and their owners are trained there.

Training a guide dog

Training a guide dog takes time and a lot of effort. There are five stages in this important training. Most guide dogs are fully trained at about two years of age.

1. *Preparation for puppy-walking*
   From six weeks of age the puppies are brought to the training centre where they are examined by a vet. The pups are micro-chipped and begin to be house trained.

2. *Puppy-walking*
   Volunteers foster the puppies for 12–15 months. These puppy-walking volunteers help the puppy become obedient and used to people and other animals.

3. *Early Training*
   When a puppy is about one year old, it leaves its puppy-walker and joins other dogs at the training centre. Specially trained instructors work with the dogs every day for three to five months. Each dog is taught how to stop at a kerb, when to cross roads and how to avoid obstacles. They are brought into the city to get used to traffic and noise. They are taken into shops and restaurants and onto buses and trains and into lifts.

4. *Advanced Training*

If the dog completes Early Training successfully, it will be trained for another three months. This is called Advanced Training and the dog learns how to guide a blind or a partially-sighted person. The instructor also looks carefully at the dog's personality, and checks if it walks quickly or slowly and if it is more suited to working in the city or the country. All of this information helps to match each dog with a suitable owner in order to make the best partnership.

5. *Matching and Qualifying*

At 20–24 months of age, the dog is ready to begin work as a fully trained guide or assistance dog. The dog and its owner spend three weeks working in the training centre before going home together.

A guide dog retires at about 10 years of age.

To find out more about the work of Irish Guide Dogs for the Blind, you can check the following website: www.guidedogs.ie

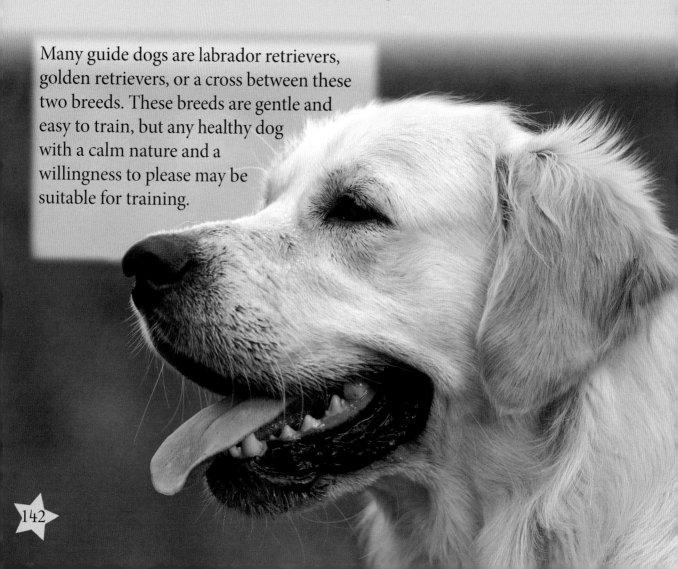

Many guide dogs are labrador retrievers, golden retrievers, or a cross between these two breeds. These breeds are gentle and easy to train, but any healthy dog with a calm nature and a willingness to please may be suitable for training.

A guide dog is on duty whenever its harness is on and it is important not to try to pet or talk to the dog while it is working.

The special harness is only worn when the dog is working. The owner can feel when the dog reaches a step or a slope in the path.

A trained dog can help a person to feel more calm, confident and secure.

1. There are five stages in training a guide dog. Describe what happens during each stage.
2. How do you think a guide dog's owner feels when his/her dog has to retire?
3. Guide dogs are working dogs. What other work can dogs do?

All the Dogs

Matthew Sweeney

You should have seen him –
he stood in the park and whistled,
underneath an oak tree,
and all the dogs came bounding up
and sat around him,
keeping their big eyes on him,
tails going like pendulums.
And there was one cocker pup
who went and licked his hand,
and a Labrador who whimpered
till the rest joined in.

Then he whistled a second time,
high-pitched as a stoat,
over all the shouted dog names
and whistles of owners,
till a flurry of paws
brought more dogs, panting,
as if they'd come miles,
and these too found space
on the flattened grass
to stare at the boy's
unmemorable face
which all the dogs found special.

My Dog

Max Fatchen

My dog is such a gentle soul
  Although he's big it's true.
He brings me the paper in his mouth,
  He brings the postman too.

1. Have you read this book or seen the film? Tell the class about it.
2. Do you like Roald Dahl's stories and poems? Why?
3. Look at the illustrations and make a prediction about what will happen in this chapter.
4. There are lots of interesting words in this story. As you read, pick out words that are new or that appeal to you.

Matilda

Roald Dahl

Chapter three: Miss Honey

Matilda was a little late in starting school. Most children begin Primary School at five or even just before, but Matilda's parents, who weren't very concerned one way or the other about their daughter's education, had forgotten to make the proper arrangements in advance. She was five and a half when she entered school for the first time.

The village school for younger children was a bleak brick building called Crunchem Hall Primary School. It had about two hundred and fifty pupils aged from five to just under twelve years old. The head teacher, the boss, the supreme commander of this establishment was a formidable middle-aged lady whose name was Miss Trunchbull. ⭐

⭐ What mood is created on this page? What words help to build this mood?

Naturally Matilda was put in the bottom class, where there were eighteen other small boys and girls about the same age as her. Their teacher was called Miss Honey, and she could not have been more than twenty-three or twenty-four. She had a lovely pale oval madonna face with blue eyes and her hair was light-brown. Her body was so slim and fragile one got the feeling that if she fell over she would smash into a thousand pieces, like a porcelain figure.

Miss Jennifer Honey was a mild and quiet person who never raised her voice and was seldom seen to smile, but there is no doubt she possessed that rare gift for being adored by every small child under her care. She seemed to understand totally the bewilderment and fear that so often overwhelms young children who for the first time in their lives are herded into a classroom and told to obey orders. Some curious warmth that was almost tangible shone out of Miss Honey's face when she spoke to a confused and homesick newcomer to the class.

Miss Trunchbull, the Headmistress, was something else altogether. She was a gigantic holy terror, a fierce tyrannical monster who frightened the life out of the pupils and teachers alike. There was an aura of menace about her even at a distance, and when she came up close you could almost feel the dangerous heat radiating from her as from a red-hot rod of metal. When she marched – Miss Trunchbull never walked, she always marched like a storm-trooper with long strides and arms aswinging – when she marched along a corridor you could actually hear her snorting as she went, and if a group of children happened to be in her path, she ploughed right on through them like a tank, with small people bouncing off her to left and right. Thank goodness we don't meet many people like her in this world, although they do exist and all of us are likely to come across at least one of them in a lifetime. If you ever do, you should behave as you would if you met an enraged rhinoceros out in the bush – climb up the nearest tree and stay there until it has gone away.

This woman, in all her eccentricities and in her appearance, is almost impossible to describe, but I shall make some attempt to do so a little later on.

Let us leave her for the moment and go back to Matilda and her first day in Miss Honey's class.

After the usual business of going through all the names of the children, Miss Honey handed out a brand-new exercise-book to each pupil.

'You have all brought your own pencils, I hope,' she said.

'Yes, Miss Honey,' they chanted.

Compare the descriptions of Miss Honey and Miss Trunchbull.

'Good. Now this is the very first day of school for each one of you. It is the beginning of at least eleven long years of schooling that all of you are going to have to go through. And six of those years will be spent right here at Crunchem Hall where, as you know, your Headmistress is Miss Trunchbull. Let me for your own good tell you something about Miss Trunchbull. She insists upon strict discipline throughout the school, and if you take my advice you will do your very best to behave yourselves in her presence. Never argue with her. Never answer her back. Always do as she says. If you get on the wrong side of Miss Trunchbull she can liquidise you like a carrot in a kitchen blender. It's nothing to laugh about, Lavender. Take that grin off your face. All of you will be wise to remember that Miss Trunchbull deals very very severely with anyone who gets out of line in this school. Have you got the message?'

'Yes, Miss Honey,' chirruped eighteen eager little voices.

'I myself,' Miss Honey went on, 'want to help you to learn as much as possible while you are in this class. That is because I know it will make things easier for you later on. For example, by the end of this week I shall expect every one of you to know the two-times table by heart. And in a year's time I hope you will know all the multiplication tables up to twelve. It will help you enormously if you do. Now then, do any of you happen to have learnt the two-times table already?'

Matilda put up her hand. She was the only one.

Miss Honey looked carefully at the tiny girl with dark hair and a round serious face sitting in the second row.

'Wonderful,' she said. 'Please stand up and recite as much of it as you can.'

Matilda stood up and began to say the two times table. When she got to twice twelve is twenty-four she didn't stop. She went right on with twice thirteen is twenty-six, twice fourteen is twenty-eight, twice fifteen is thirty, twice sixteen is ...

'Stop!' Miss Honey said. She had been listening slightly spellbound to this smooth recital, and now she said, 'How far can you go?'

'How far?' Matilda said. 'Well, I don't really know, Miss Honey. For quite a long way, I think.'

Miss Honey took a few moments to let this curious statement sink in. 'You mean,' she said, 'that you could tell me what two times twenty-eight is?'

'Yes, Miss Honey.'

'What is it?'

'Fifty-six, Miss Honey.'

How would you describe the atmosphere on this page?

'What about something much harder, like two times four hundred and eighty-seven? Could you tell me that?'

'I think so, yes,' Matilda said.

'Are you sure?'

'Why yes, Miss Honey, I'm fairly sure.'

'What is it then, two times four hundred and eighty-seven?'

'Nine hundred and seventy-four,' Matilda said immediately. She spoke quietly and politely and without any sign of showing off.

Miss Honey gazed at Matilda with absolute amazement, but when next she spoke she kept her voice level. 'That is really splendid,' she said. 'But of course multiplying by two is a lot easier than some of the bigger numbers. What about the other multiplication tables? Do you know any of those?'

'I think so, Miss Honey. I think I do.'

'Which ones, Matilda? How far have you got?'

'I ... I don't quite know,' Matilda said. 'I don't know what you mean.'

'What I mean is do you for instance know the three-times tables?'

'Yes, Miss Honey.'

'And the four-times?'

'Yes, Miss Honey.'

'Well, how many do you know, Matilda? Do you know all the way up to the twelve-times table?'

'Yes, Miss Honey.'

'What are twelve sevens?'

What do you imagine the other children think of Matilda?

'Eighty-four,' Matilda said.

Miss Honey paused and leaned back in her chair behind the plain table that stood in the middle of the floor in front of the class. She was considerably shaken by this exchange but took care not to show it. She had never come across a five-year-old before, or indeed a ten-year-old, who could multiply with such facility.

'I hope the rest of you are listening to this,' she said to the class. 'Matilda is a very lucky girl. She has wonderful parents who have already taught her to multiply lots of numbers. Was it your mother, Matilda, who taught you?'

'No, Miss Honey, it wasn't.'

'You must have a great father then. He must be a brilliant teacher.'

'No, Miss Honey,' Matilda said quietly. 'My father did not teach me.'

'You mean you taught yourself?'

'I don't quite know,' Matilda said truthfully.

'It's just that I don't find it very difficult to multiply one number by another.'

How do you think Matilda knows all the answers?

1. What is the name of Matilda's school?
2. How many pupils are in Matilda's class?

3. Find words used in the extract to describe Miss Trunchbull.
4. Discuss the interesting or new words that appealed to you as you read through the chapter.
5. The author makes good use of dialogue in this chapter. What do we learn about the characters from the dialogue?

6. How do you think Matilda felt on her first day?
7. What do you think is the funniest part of the chapter?
8. Do you think Matilda is showing off? Give reasons for your answer.
9. What impressions do you have of Matilda's parents?
10. How do you think Miss Honey gets on with Miss Trunchbull?
11. Do you think the author is having fun with names in this story? Talk about it.

12. Have you read other stories set in a school? Tell the class.
13. What subject would you like to be brilliant at? Why?
14. Can you remember how you felt on your first day of school?

I Think My Teacher Is a Cowboy

John Coldwell

It's not just
That she rides to school on a horse
And carries a Colt 45 in her handbag.

It's not just
the way she walks;
hands hanging over her hips.

It's not just
the way she dresses;
stetson hat and spurs on her boots.

It's not just the way she talks;
calling the playground the corral,
  the Head's room the Sheriff's office,
  the school canteen the chuck wagon,
  the school bus the stagecoach
  the bike sheds the livery stable.

What gives her away
Is when the hometime pips go.
She slaps her thigh
And cries
'Yee ha!'

First Day at School

Roger McGough

A millionbillionwillion miles from home.
Waiting for the bell to go. (To go where?)
Why are they all so big, other children?
So noisy? So much at home they
must have been born in uniform.
Lived all their lives in playgrounds
Spent the years inventing games
That don't let me in. Games
That are rough, that swallow you up.

And the railings.
All around, the railings.
Are they to keep out wolves and monsters?
Things that carry off and eat children?

Things you don't take sweets from?
Perhaps they're to stop us getting out.
Running away from the lessins. Lessin.
What does a lessin look like?
Sounds small and slimy.
They keep them in glassrooms.
Whole rooms made out of glass. Imagine.

I wish I could remember my name.
Mummy said it would come in useful.
Like wellies. Then there's puddles.
Yellowwellies. I wish she was here.
I think my name is sewn on somewhere.
Perhaps the teacher will read it for me.
Tea-cher. The one who makes the tea.

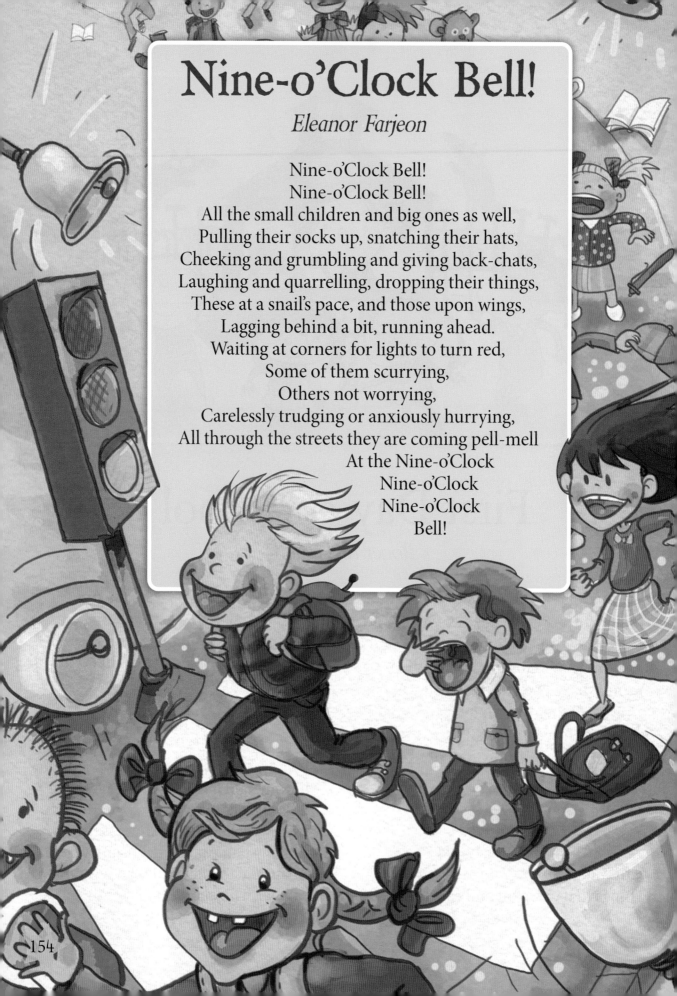

Nine-o'Clock Bell!

Eleanor Farjeon

Nine-o'Clock Bell!
Nine-o'Clock Bell!
All the small children and big ones as well,
Pulling their socks up, snatching their hats,
Cheeking and grumbling and giving back-chats,
Laughing and quarrelling, dropping their things,
These at a snail's pace, and those upon wings,
Lagging behind a bit, running ahead.
Waiting at corners for lights to turn red,
Some of them scurrying,
Others not worrying,
Carelessly trudging or anxiously hurrying,
All through the streets they are coming pell-mell
At the Nine-o'Clock
Nine-o'Clock
Nine-o'Clock
Bell!

1. Have you read any part of *Alice in Wonderland* before or seen the film? If so, tell the class about it.
2. Where do you imagine Wonderland is?
3. Examine the artwork. How can you tell that this is a fantasy story?

Alice in Wonderland

Lewis Carroll

The Queen's Croquet Ground

A large rose-tree stood near the entrance of the garden: the roses growing on it were white, but there were three gardeners at it, busily painting them red. Alice thought this a very curious thing, and she went nearer to watch them, and just as she came up to them she heard one of them say, 'Look out now, Five! Don't go splashing paint over me like that!'

'I couldn't help it,' said Five, in a sulky tone. 'Seven jogged my elbow.'

On which Seven looked up and said 'That's right, Five! Always lay the blame on others!'

'*You'd* better not talk!' said Five. 'I heard the Queen say only yesterday you deserved to be beheaded!'

'What for?' said the one who had spoken first.

'That's none of *your* business, Two!' said Seven.

'Yes, it is his business!' said Five. 'And I'll tell him – it was for bringing the cook tulip-roots instead of onions.'

Seven flung down his brush, and had just begun 'Well of all the unjust things –' when his eye chanced to fall upon Alice, as she stood watching them, and he checked himself suddenly: the others looked round also, and all of them bowed low.

'Would you tell me, please,' said Alice, a little timidly, 'why you are painting those roses?'

Five and Seven said nothing, but looked at Two. Two began in a low voice, 'Why, the fact is, you see, Miss, this here ought to have been a *red* rose-tree, and we put a white one in by mistake; and if the Queen was to find it out, we should all have our heads cut off, you know. So you see, Miss, we're doing our best, afore she comes, to –' At this moment Five who had been anxiously looking across the garden, called out 'The Queen! The Queen!' and the three gardeners instantly threw themselves flat upon their faces. There was a sound of many footsteps, and Alice looked round, eager to see the Queen.

First came ten soldiers carrying clubs: these were all shaped like the three gardeners, oblong and flat, with their hands and feet at the corners: next the ten courtiers: these were ornamented all over with diamonds, and walked two and two, as the soldiers did. After these came the royal children: there were ten of them, and the little dears came jumping merrily along, hand in hand, in couples: they were all ornamented with hearts. Next came the guests, mostly Kings and Queens, and among them Alice recognised the White Rabbit: it was talking in a hurried nervous manner smiling at everything that was said, and went by without noticing her. Then followed the Knave of Hearts, carrying the king's crown on a crimson velvet cushion; and, last of all in this grand procession, came THE KING AND QUEEN OF HEARTS.

Alice was rather doubtful whether she ought not to lie down on her face like the three gardeners, but she could not remember ever having heard of such a rule at processions; 'and besides, what would be the use of a procession,' thought she, 'if people had all to lie down on their faces, so that they couldn't see it?' So she stood where she was, and waited.

☆ How has the author created a picture of the Queen before she appears?

When the procession came opposite to Alice, they all stopped and looked at her, and the Queen said severely, 'Who is this?' She said it to the Knave of Hearts, who only bowed and smiled in reply.

'Idiot!' said the Queen, tossing her head impatiently; and turning to Alice, she went on, 'What's your name, child?'

'My name is Alice, so please your Majesty,' said Alice very politely; but she added, to herself, 'Why, they're only a pack of cards, after all. I needn't be afraid of them!'

'And who are *these*?' said the Queen, pointing to the three gardeners who were lying round the rose-tree; for, you see, as they were lying on their faces, and the pattern on their backs was the same as the rest of the pack, she could not tell whether they were gardeners, or soldiers, or courtiers, or three of her own children.

'How should *I* know?' said Alice, surprised at her own courage. 'It's no business of *mine*.'

The Queen turned crimson with fury, and, after glaring at her for a moment like a wild beast, began screaming 'Off with her head! Off with –'

'Nonsense!' said Alice, very loudly and decidedly, and the Queen was silent.

The King laid his hand upon her arm, and timidly said 'Consider, my dear: she is only a child!'

The Queen turned angrily away from him, and said to the Knave 'Turn them over!'

The Knave did so, very carefully, with one foot.

'Get up!' said the Queen, in a shrill, loud voice, and the three gardeners instantly jumped up, and began bowing to the King, the Queen, the royal children, and everybody else.

'Leave off that!' screamed the Queen. 'You make me giddy.' And then, turning to the rose-tree, she went on, 'What *have* you been doing here?'

'May it please your Majesty,' said Two, in a very humble tone, going down on one knee as he spoke, 'we were trying –'

'*I* see!' said the Queen, who had meanwhile been examining the roses. 'Off with their heads!' and the procession moved on, three of the soldiers remaining behind to execute the unfortunate gardeners, who ran to Alice for protection.

'You shan't be beheaded!' said Alice, and she put them into a large flower-pot that stood near. The three soldiers wandered about for a minute or two, looking for

Do you agree that Alice shows courage. Why?

How would you describe the Queen's attitude towards her subjects?

them, and then quietly marched off after the others.

'Are their heads off?' shouted the Queen.

'Their heads are gone, if it please your Majesty!' the soldiers shouted in reply.

'That's right!' shouted the Queen. 'Can you play croquet?'

The soldiers were silent, and looked at Alice, as the question was evidently meant for her.

'Yes!' shouted Alice.

'Come on, then!' roared the Queen and Alice joined the procession, wondering very much what would happen next.

'It's – it's a very fine day!' said a timid voice at her side. She was walking by the White Rabbit, who was peeping anxiously into her face.

'Very,' said Alice. 'Where's the Duchess?'

'Hush! Hush!' said the Rabbit in a low hurried tone. He looked anxiously over his shoulder as he spoke, and then raise himself upon tiptoe, put his mouth close to her ear, and whispered 'She's under sentence of execution.'

'What for?' said Alice.

'Did you say "What a pity!"?' the Rabbit asked.

'No, I didn't,' said Alice. 'I don't think it's at all a pity. I said "What for?"'

'She boxed the Queen's ears –' the Rabbit began. Alice gave a little scream of laughter. 'Oh, hush!' the Rabbit whispered in a frightened tone. 'The Queen will hear you! You see she came rather late, and the Queen said –'

'Get to your places!' shouted the Queen in a voice of thunder, and people began running about in all directions, tumbling up against each other: however, they got settled down in a minute or two, and the game began. Alice thought she had never seen such a curious croquet ground in all her life: it was all ridges and furrows: the balls were live hedgehogs, and the mallets live flamingos, and the soldiers had to double themselves up and stand on their hands and feet, to make the arches.

The chief difficulty Alice found at first was in managing her flamingo: she succeeded in getting its body tucked away, comfortably enough, under her arm, with its legs hanging down, but generally, just as she had got its neck nicely straightened out, and was going to give the hedgehog a blow with its head, it *would* twist itself round and look up in her face, with such a puzzled expression that she could not help bursting out laughing; and when she had got its head down and was going to begin again, it was very provoking to find that the hedgehog had unrolled itself, and was in the act of crawling away: besides all this, there was generally a ridge or furrow in the way wherever she wanted to send the hedgehog to, and, as the doubled-up soldiers were always getting up and walking off to other parts of the ground, Alice soon came to the conclusion that it was a very difficult game indeed.

1. What were the gardeners doing?
2. What were the names of the gardeners?
3. Describe the soldiers and courtiers.
4. What were the flamingos and hedgehogs used for?

5. Do you think this chapter is funny? What parts do you like best?
6. This story is a fantasy. Find evidence of this in the extract.
7. There is a lot of dialogue in this story. How does it help us get to know the characters?

8. Do you think Alice is brave to speak out? What would you do? Why?
9. Who do you think is the most important character in the extract? Why?
10. Lewis Carroll shows great imagination in bringing the playing cards to life. Do you agree?

11. Invent a game or create a fantasy version of a game you know. Describe it.

Roman life

1. What is your favourite pastime?
2. How do you think your parents or your grandparents entertained themselves when they were younger?

If you want to relax after school, or at the weekend, there are lots of things that you can do to amuse yourself. You can watch television, play a game of football, go to the cinema, play a computer game or read a book.

The ancient Romans had very different ideas about entertainment. Two of their favourite pastimes were going to the Colosseum and going to the Circus Maximus.

The Colosseum

This was a huge stadium that could seat 50,000 people. Here there were many spectacular but often very cruel shows.

In the Colosseum, men, women and animals fought, usually to the death. Many of those taking part were criminals or prisoners-of-war but some were innocent slaves. Christians were forced to fight in the Colosseum because the Romans were afraid of the new Christian faith. Many Christians were eaten by lions.

Rome also had hundreds of professional fighters, called *gladiators*. 'Gladius' is the Roman word for 'sword'. If a fighter lost but had shown great courage, the Emperor might spare his or her life. He signalled this by raising his thumb. Today we still have the expression 'to give the thumbs up'.

Like most entertainment in Rome, entrance to the Colosseum was free. Once inside, men were separated from women, with the men seated closer to the arena! At the very back of the Colosseum there was standing room for slaves.

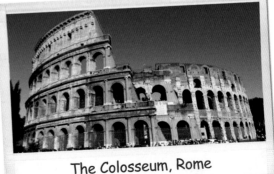

The Colosseum, Rome

Circus Maximus

This was where Romans went to see chariot races. The Circus Maximus was the largest chariot racing track in the Roman Empire and could seat up to 250,000 people. This is about three times the size of Croke Park in Dublin!

People queued up early in the morning to get the best seats. Slaves were not allowed to attend the Circus Maximus. Sometimes the Emperor himself would attend to start the races. This caused great excitement.

There were twenty-four races a day with up to twelve chariots in each race. Each chariot raced for one of four teams: the Reds, the Whites, the Greens or the Blues. Spectators supported their favourite team with great loyalty and fights often took place during the races.

Chariot-racing was very dangerous. The chariots raced around the track and often crashed into each other, especially when speeding around the bends. The winning charioteer received a palm leaf together with a purse of gold. The bravest and fastest drivers became famous throughout Rome, like the film stars and pop stars of today.

1. Compare the Colosseum with the Circus Maximus under these headings:
   a.) size   b.) dangers involved   c.) spectators
2. Which would you prefer to have been, a gladiator or a charioteer? Why?

The ROMAN Chronicle

Sunday 18 March 44 BC

3 denarii

CAESAR KILLED

Brutus leads assassins

Chief journalist – Llaricus Juleluis

JULIUS CAESAR, the Emperor of Rome, was STABBED to death in parliament on Thursday.

Caesar had just gone into the parliament when the attack came. Over 20 senators crowded round him. Each one stabbed Caesar at least once.

They were part of a cold-blooded plan to murder Caesar. He tried to fight back, but they were too strong for him.

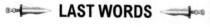 **LAST WORDS**

Caesar's old friend, Brutus, was one of the killers. Caesar's dying words were 'And you Brutus?'

The Emperor's body lay where it fell for most of the day. At last three slaves carried it home.

BETRAYED: Caesar murdered by his jealous friends

Caesar had been **WARNED** of danger some time ago, but he was not a man to run from danger.

Caesar's death rocks Rome	pages 1 and 2
Roman news	page 3
Obituary	page 4
Empire news	pages 5 and 6
Money	page 7
Lifestyle	page 8
Women's page	page 9
Comment	page 10
Letters	page 11
Home & Health	page 12
For Sale	page 13
Sport	pages 14, 15 and 16

162

BLUES BLAZE TO VICTORY

LAST WEEK'S crowd at the Circus Maximus saw the best racing of the year. 250,000 race fans came to cheer their teams – and gasp at the crashes.

The day started with races for small two-horse chariots. Rome's home teams, the Blues and Whites, won easily. Then, as the day hotted up, so did the race fever. The mid-day race was a scorcher.

HORSEPOWER: Philip shows his star starting style

RACE FEVER

Four Roman teams, and four out-of-town teams lined up at the start. The horses bucked and stamped. The starter's flag went up. The huge crowd held its breath. Then the gates went up – and the crowd went wild.

DEATH

The pack flew round the first lap of this eight-kilometre race. The crowd cheered as Rome's Claudius went in front. The cheers soon turned to groans. Another Roman driver cut in too soon and flipped over. With his reins tied round his chest, he was dragged to his death.

WINNING POST

Then, two laps later, the Roman Blues took the lead. Their new driver, Philip, kept it to the end. The crowd roared as he flashed past the winning post. They'd just seen a new star driver win his first race.

WATCH THIS SPACE!

But it won't be his last – you can bet on that.

1. Look at an Irish newspaper. How is the front page similar or different?
2. Pick out words and phrases that build up the action in the 'Blues Blaze to Victory' piece.

1. What do you know about life in ancient Rome? Talk about it in class.
2. Read the introduction. Do you know about any other Roman emperors?
3. How do you think Marcus's family will react to the horse being brought to their home?

WANTED!

Kate Thompson

Young Marcus lived in ancient Rome when the crazy Gaius – nicknamed Littleboots – ruled as emperor. One of the strangest things that Gaius did was to appoint his favourite horse Incitatus (In-si-ta-tus) as one of Rome's two consuls. The consuls were the most important officials in the city! One day, while he is delivering bread for his father's bakery business, Marcus ends up minding the horse and when he is spotted by soldiers he jumps on the horse's back and escapes to the safety of home. Shortly afterwards his brother Lucius and cousin Quintus come in with some amazing news: they have heard that the emperor has just died.

You would expect us to celebrate, perhaps, to clap and cheer and dance around the compound with delight. We didn't. Instead a silence fell over us, so profound that even the dogs stopped their energetic activities and slumped down in the dust. Behind the bakery doors, Incitatus whickered anxiously, and I heard the thud-thud-thud of more of his golden droppings landing on the spotless floor. Every one of us hoped that what we had heard was true, but every one of us, from my aged grandmother right down to my seven-year-old cousin, was thinking the same thing.

It was a trick.

It would be just like Littleboots to do something like that. Spread the word that he was dead and then, while people were celebrating and sacrificing victims to the gods, send out his soldiers to arrest them all for disloyalty. Then he could confiscate their property and use the proceeds to finance his vile appetites, and send them to the Circus Maximus to fight his professional gladiators, or cut off their hands and string them round their necks, or feed them to his lions and alligators and other dreadful beasts.

But we would not fall into that trap. We stayed silent. Incitatus whickered again and I opened one of the doors so he could see us.

'We continue as usual,' said my grandmother at last. She spoke softly, afraid of eavesdroppers. 'We do nothing and say nothing until we smell the smoke from his funeral pyre.' ⭐

'Not even then,' said my father. 'I would need more proof than that.'

'Who will be emperor next?' said my little sister, Tiberia.

'Shh,' said my mother. 'Hold your tongue.'

We had a plan then, about how to react to the rumour. But we still had a serious problem on our hands.

'What are we going to do about the consul?' I said.

'The best plan,' said my father, 'is to wait until dark, then strip all the finery off him and turn him out on to the street.'

'That kind of plan never works,' said my mother. 'There's always some child or a nosy old sweeper who's bound to see you. And what would it look like, turning loose a perfectly good horse?'

My grandmother agreed. 'He'd have us in our own ovens if he ever found out we did that.'

'In any case,' I said, 'he likes us. If we turned him out he wouldn't go anywhere. He'd just stand outside the gates until we let him back in.'

My aunt glared at me, but she didn't say anything.

'So there's two choices, as far as I can see,' said my mother. 'We take him back to

What does Marcus's Grandmother mean by this?

the palace and hand him over, or we keep him here, hidden away, until we discover what has happened.'

'There's another thing we can do,' said hard man Quintus. 'We can cut him up and feed him to the dogs.'

Lucius grinned. 'That would serve Littleboots right.'

My grandmother stepped forward into our midst. 'Now listen, all of you,' she said. 'That boy' – she poked me hard in the collarbone – 'came riding in here this afternoon at a very high speed. The horse is wearing a purple robe and a head collar dripping with jewels. Does everyone here really believe that no one will have noticed?'

Everyone didn't. When we stopped to think about it, no one did.

'Someone, somewhere, knows that Incitatus is here,' my grandmother went on. 'So losing him or feeding him to the dogs will do us no good.' ⭐

Quintus shrugged, but everyone else nodded, and my grandmother continued: 'It's my opinion that your son, my own grandson, signed a death sentence for everyone in this family when he brought Incitatus to these gates.'

My heart stopped and my breath got stuck in my throat. I felt as though I was already standing in front of Littleboots, waiting to hear what particular horrors he had chosen for me.

'No!' I managed to blurt.

'He didn't mean it,' said my mother, moving closer to me.

'Always the same,' said my grandmother. 'Never stops to think.'

'Well, what would you have done in his position?' asked my mother indignantly.

'What I would have done is beside the point,' said my grandmother.

'It's what we do now that will decide whether we live or die.'

'And that is ...?' said my father.

'We treat the consul as an honoured guest. You invite him into your house and give him the best bedroom.'

'My house!' said my father. 'Why not your house?'

'Because mine is humble and small and yours is large and elegant. Or at least, it used to be when I lived in it.'

He had to concede the point. 'And what then?' he said. 'What happens if they discover him here?' ⭐

⭐ What is your impression of the grandmother at this point in the story?

⭐ Do you think Marcus's father is as strong a character as his grandmother?

'Then we tell the truth. We say that we heard dreadful rumours concerning the health of the emperor, and your son witnessed unrest and violence not far from the palace. For the consul's own safety he invited him to reside with us until the situation settled down and the true facts become known.'

'I invited him?' I said.

'Indeed you did,' said my grandmother.

'And he most graciously accepted.'

---

1. What was everybody's reaction to the news that the emperor was dead?
2. What did Quintus suggest that they should do with the horse?

3. Name all the family members mentioned in the story.
4. Everyone was afraid of the emperor. Find sentences that show this.
5. Would you say Marcus and his family were cautious? Why do you think this?
6. Some of the family said things that were not appreciated by others. Find some examples.
7. The grandmother speaks very bluntly. Where can you see this in the chapter?

8. Who do you think is the main character in the chapter? Why do you think this?
9. What would you have done with the horse?
10. How do you think Marcus gets on with his grandmother? Find sentences that show this.

11. This story tells about a crisis in a family. Talk about any book you have read or film you have seen where there is a crisis within the family.
12. 'Marcus's heart stopped and his breath got stuck in his throat.' Has this ever happened to you? Talk about it.

A holiday by the sea

The Murphy family are planning a holiday by the sea. They are deciding where to stay. Have a look at the options below. Which holiday destination would you pick?

Accommodation	🛏	🖵	⛁	♿	🎣	🎵	S$_C$	B$_B$	F$_B$	€
Slieve Ard Hotel	45	•	•	•	•	•		•	•	70
Ballymore Lodge	23	•	•	•	•				•	55
Atlantic Inn	15	•	•	•			•		•	38
Dolphin Bay Hotel	100	•	•	•	•	•			•	60
Dunbeg Holiday Homes	4	•					•			50
Oakwood Country Club	41	•	•						•	85
Ocean View Hotel	63	•	•	•	•	•			•	50
Silver Strand Guesthouse	10							•		35
Lakeside Cottages	3						•			55
Connemara Guesthouse	12	•		•					•	40
Bayside Adventure Centre	40	•	•	•	•		•			55

The Murphys choose to have a holiday at the Bayside Adventure Centre. Here are some of the exciting activities on offer.

Abseiling

Learn to make a controlled and breath-taking descent down our purpose built 12 meter tower. A maximum of twelve people allowed (two people abseil at a time) per 1 ½ hour session.

Zip wire

Challenge yourself: leap off the top of the tower and zip wire down a 100 metre long cable. This is a great adrenaline-pumping activity. You just harness up, clip in and away you go.

Archery

This activity is designed to be a fun introduction to this sport, for 10+ only. Everyone should be able to hit the target by the end of the session. Groups of four people take part in each hourly session and this must be booked in advance.

Kayaking

This activity is for confident swimmers only and takes place in the bay. Our experienced instructors will teach you how to stay safe and how to manage your craft using a double paddle. Our instructors will test your skills with a fun and exciting range of games and group tasks. You will then explore the bay area – you may even see some local wildlife such as seals, otters and even dolphins!

Horseriding and trekking

Enjoy a gentle trek along the lanes and through the wood; more experienced riders can enjoy a canter on the beach at low tide. Two quiet ponies are available for younger children who might prefer to stay in our paddock at Bayside Stables.

Table tennis

Our table tennis area has four tables and can be booked hourly outside competition times. Register for our Youngsters vs Oldsters tournament and enjoy the Friday night championship! Bats and balls supplied (deposit required).

1. List a.) the three most expensive, b.) the three least expensive places to stay.
2. Which hotels have a swimming pool but do not provide evening entertainment?
3. Which hotels have wheelchair access and evening entertainment?
4. Which activities would you choose to do at Bayside? Why?

Acknowledgements

Fiction

The Diary of a Killer Cat by Anne Fine © Anne Fine 1994. Cover art from DIARY OF A KILLER CAT by Anne Fine © Penguin 2011

Diary of a Wimpy Kid: The Last Straw by Jeff Kinney published by Puffin Books (London, 2009). Copyright © Jeff Kinney, 2009; cover image © Puffin Books 2009

Girl in Goal by Rob Childs, taken from Literacy World Fiction Stage 2: Take a Run and Jump, by permission of Pearson Education Ltd.

The Sheep-Pig by Dick King-Smith reproduced by permission of AP Watt Ltd on behalf of Fox Busters Ltd. Illustrations © Mike Terry, reproduced by permission of the illustrator.

Charlotte's Web by E.B. White reprinted by permission of International Creative Management, Inc. Copyright © 1952 by E.B. White.

The Gold Cross of Killadoo by John Quinn reprinted by permission of Poolbeg.

Extract from *The Story of Tracy Beaker* by Jacqueline Wilson, published by Corgi Yearling reprinted by permission of The Random House Group Ltd.

THE LION, THE WITCH AND THE WARDROBE by C.S. Lewis; copyright © C.S. Lewis Pte. Ltd. 1950. Extract reprinted by permission. Illustrations by Pauline Baynes, copyright © C.S. Lewis Pte. Ltd. 1950. Reprinted by permission.

This is Not Earth © Tony Bradman and A&C Black Publishers, an imprint of Bloomsbury Publishing Plc.

Stone Fox text copyright © 1980 by John Reynolds Gardiner. Illustrations copyright © 1980 by Marcia Sewall. Used by permission of HarperCollins Publishers.

Dear Norman by Robert H. Richard taken from Independent Story of the Year 2, published by Scholastic Ltd.

Matilda by Roald Dahl (Jonathan Cape and Penguin), used by permission of David Higham Associates.

Alice in Wonderland by Lewis Carroll. Illustration copyright © 2002 by The Templar Company Limited. Used with kind permission.

Extract from *Wanted!* by Kate Thompson, published by Bodley Head Children's Books. Reprinted by permission of The Random House Group Ltd.

Poetry

'Dad and the Cat and the Tree', illustrations © Emma Chichester Clark from THE PUFFIN BOOK OF FANTASTIC FIRST POEMS, 2000 (Puffin). Permission granted by the Artist.

'Blake's Tyger – Revisited' by Michaela Morgan reprinted by permission of the author.

Twelve lines from 'Picking Teams', taken from PLEASE MRS BUTLER by Allan Ahlberg (Kestrel 1983, Puffin Books 1984) Text copyright © Allan Ahlberg, 1983.

'The Sheep' by Seumas O'Sullivan reprinted by permission of Frances Sommerville.

'Chocolate Cake' by Michael Rosen reprinted by permission of Penguin Books Ltd.

'Good Company' by Leonard Clark, reproduced by permission of the Literary Executor of Leonard Clark.

'Sailing' by David English taken from Macmillan Treasury Children's Poems.

'My Rocket Dreamed' by Paul Cookson reproduced by permission of the author.

'My Dog' Copyright © Max Fatchen, *Wry Rhymes for Troublesome Times* 1983. Reproduced with permission of Johnson & Alcock Ltd.

'First Day at School' by Roger McGough from *In the Glassroom* (© Roger McGough, 1976) is printed by permission of United Agents (www.unitedagents.co.uk) on behalf of Roger McGough.

'Nine-o'Clock Bell!' by Eleanor Farjeon, taken from *Blackbird Has Spoken*, published by Macmillan Children's Books © 2000.

'Thank-you Letter' by Robin Klein reproduced by arrangement with Robin Klein, c/o Curtis Brown (Aust) Pty Ltd.

Drama

Roald Dahl's *Charlie and the Chocolate Factory* - A play adapted by Richard R. George (Penguin), used by permission of David Higham Associates.

The publishers have made every effort to contact copyright holders but any omission will be rectified at the next reprint.

Picture Credits

For permission to reproduce photographs, the authors and publisher gratefully acknowledge the following:

© Alamy: 5B, 7TL, 7TCR, 7CR, 16C, 16B, 32, 34T, 52T, 55CT, 55CB, 55B, 64, 65, 67, 78TL, 78TR, 78CR, 91C, 91CBL, 91CBC, 91CBR, 92B, 117B, 119L, 119R, 119 background, 126TL, 126CR, 126CL, 127TL, 127CL, 127CR, 127TR, 127BR, 128TL, 142, 143TL, 143TC, 160B, 161, 168T, 168B, 169T, 169B; © Getty Images: 5T, 6T, 6B, 7TCL, 7TR, 7BR, 8, 16T, 16CR, 33B, 33T, 53TL, 53B, 54, 55T, 56B, 56T, 91BL, 92T, 116, 117T, 126B, 127BL, 128CR, 143TR, 169C, 46TL; © Inpho: 34C, 89T, 89B, 91T, 91BR; © Press Association: 15C; © Topfoto: 53TR.

The authors and publisher have made every effort to trace all copyright holders, but if any has been inadvertently overlooked, we would be pleased to make the necessary arrangement at the first opportunity.